HABARI GANI?

(How are you?)

MAMA, BABA AND MPENDWA!

(Loved ones)

Children tell time every day, but how often do they acknowledge or even think about the seminal contributions of mathematician Benjamin Banneker? It is not enough to simply know how to read the hands on a clock. Our children must have knowledge of the excellent Black mind that produced the idea. Black peoples' contributions have shaped the world, and our children must know this if we are ever to empower and uplift them. By studying what others have done, they begin to understand their own capabilities.

We created **Telling Time with Benjamin Banneker and Sekou** to start our children on a journey to learning about Benjamin Banneker and his contributions to the world. Aside from teaching the basic concepts of telling time, we also created the activity book to get our children thinking about using their knowledge to build businesses and institutions for our people. To support this effort, we have created a mini-story and coloring activities to make learning fun. This book reinforces the idea of studying the work of our ancestors and uplifting our people.

Telling Time teaches our children that the concept of time started with our African ancestors who created the shadow clock, tekhenu (obelisk), sundial, and merkhet to tell time. Benjamin Banneker and our African ancestors used their knowledge of mathematics, science and astronomy to advance the concept of time. This book seeks to encourage our children to do the same. Like our ancestors, our children are brilliant mathematicians, scientists and astronomers. We just have to stimulate and cultivate their genius.

We strongly believe Black people have to take the lead role in producing educational materials and books to uplift and empower our children. In doing research about Benjamin Banneker, it was hard to find children's books written by our people. We considered this a problem. As a people, we have to be the vanguards of our history, culture, ancestors and contributions.

WE HOPE YOU ENJOY THE ACTIVITIES!

BENJAMIN

WASHINGTON
DC

BANNEKER

Benjamin Banneker was a Black man of African heritage born in Baltimore County, MD, on November 9, 1731. Though he only attended school for a short period of time, his innate love for learning, which he surely inherited from his African ancestors, fueled his desire to read books and explore different topics, such as mathematics, science and astronomy.

Unashamed, Banneker proudly proclaimed his African heritage (like all Black people should do) and went on to become an accomplished mathematician, scientist, astronomer, surveyor, urban planner, farmer, author and publisher. He made various contributions to the world that many people fail to acknowledge, like the clock, almanac, farm irrigation system and the official survey of Washington, DC.

Benjamin Banneker's love for mathematics and science played a major role in the creation of the first wooden clock in 1752. He was 22 years old. How exactly the original idea came to be isn't clear. Some people say Banneker was inspired by a sundial and pocket watch. Others say the idea was completely his own, starting in his head and then being transferred to paper. Some people say Banneker created the clock after taking apart a watch and studying its components. No matter the account, one thing remains true: Benjamin Banneker built a quality clock that struck with precision every hour on the hour for 40 years straight. He set an example for all Black people on how to capitalize on specialized knowledge.

While Benjamin Banneker is credited with creating the first clock in America, we understand that he was inspired by our African ancestors who first created time-telling tools such as shadow clocks, tekhenu (obelisk), sundials and merkhets.

Our ancestors were the first to divide the day into different parts to tell time. Tekhenu (obelisk) were believed to first appear around 2575 B.C. and were used to tell time by reading the shadows they cast. Tekhenu (obelisk) were also built to tell a story. Around 1500 B.C., our African ancestors used the sundial as a tool to tell time. They were modified versions of the shadow clocks and provided more accurate readings by dividing the day into 10 or 12 parts. Using the stars, Merkhets were used to calculate time at night. Benjamin Banneker and our African ancestors used mathematics, astronomy and science as key tools to tell time.

Benjamin Banneker was born a free man and made many important contributions to the world during a time when many people of African descent were enslaved and treated as subhuman. His father was enslaved but was later freed. Banneker's life experiences and worldview afforded him the opportunity to speak out against slavery, prejudice and injustice. Up until his death on October 9, 1806, Banneker spent his life making important contributions to the world. The clock is one of those contributions and we celebrate it in this activity book.

AFRICAN WAYS
of
TELLING TIME

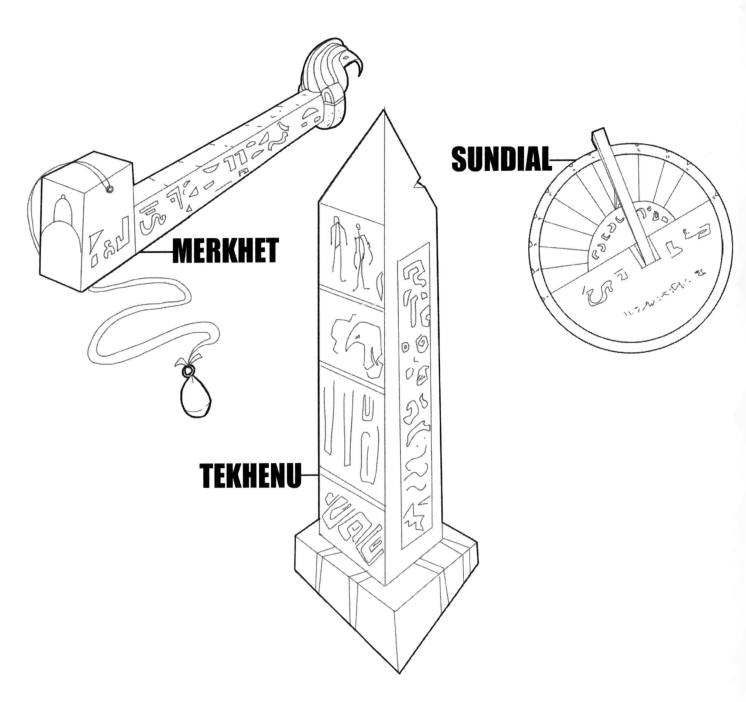

MERKHET

SUNDIAL

TEKHENU

3

SEKOU'S JOURNEY

with

BENJAMIN BANNEKER

4

Benjamin Banneker teaches Sekou about the clock components and how they function.

www.kujichaguliapress.com

Benjamin Banneker teaches Sekou how to create a clock from wooden parts.

Benjamin Banneker teaches Sekou the importance of starting your own business.

www.kujichaguliapress.com

Sekou teaches other brothers and sisters how to tell time with Benjamin Banneker.

THE BASICS OF TELLING TIME WITH A CLOCK

Time is measured by seconds, minutes, hours, days, weeks, months and years. On a clock, time is represented by seconds, minutes and hours.

Our ancestor, Benjamin Banneker, created the first analog clock to help us tell time in a precise manner. A clock with moving hands, numbered 1 to 12 to show the time, is called an analog clock. They are divided into 12 parts and each part represents five minutes, totaling 60 minutes once the minute hand travels around all 12 clock numbers (5 minutes x 12 clock numbers = 60 minutes).

Telling time with analog clocks involves regular use of mathematics, including addition, subtraction, division, multiplication and so on.

A clock measures time in hours, minutes and seconds. A clock has a long hand that represents each minute and a short hand that represents each hour. The long hand is often called the minute hand and the short hand is often called the hour hand. Although some clocks do not display seconds, they are still being counted.

The minute hand and the hour hand both move forward gradually. The minute hand moves forward every 60 seconds to the next minute. The hour hand moves forward every 60 minutes to the next clock number, which represents one complete hour. The hour hand rotates around the entire clock to every clock number until it gets to 12. When telling time, you always start by reading the hour hand (short hand). Then you read the minute (long hand).

There are 60 seconds in one minute. There are 60 minutes in one hour. There are 24 hours in one day. There are seven days in a week and four weeks in most months. There are 12 months in a year and 365 days in most years.

TELLING TIME VOCABULARY WORDS

Directions: Please work with your mtoto (child) to define the following words:

1) time

2) analog clock

3) hour

4) hour hand

5) minute

6) minute hand

7) sundial

8) tekhenu

9) merkhet

MAIN PARTS OF AN ANALOG CLOCK

HOURS

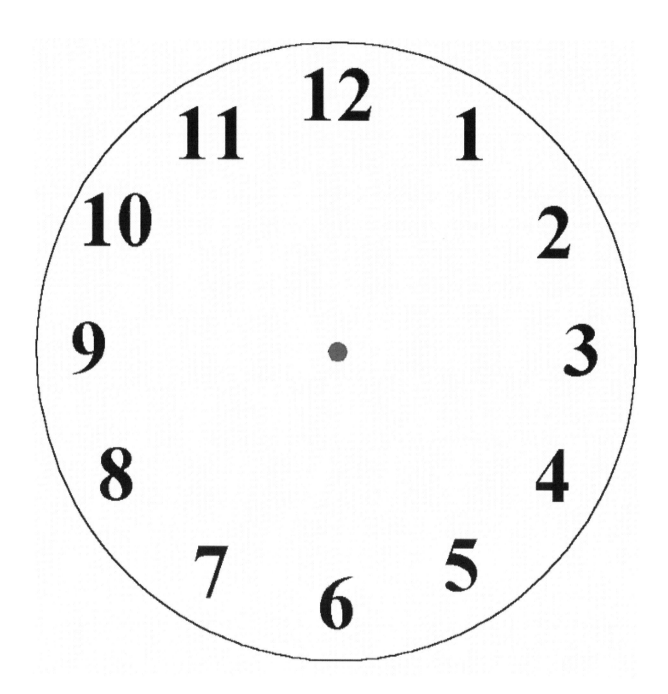

Part 1

Locate the hours on the clock. Count each hour on the clock with your mtoto (child).

The hours are represented by the large, bold clock numbers 1–12. This is the basic setup for analog clocks.

MINUTES

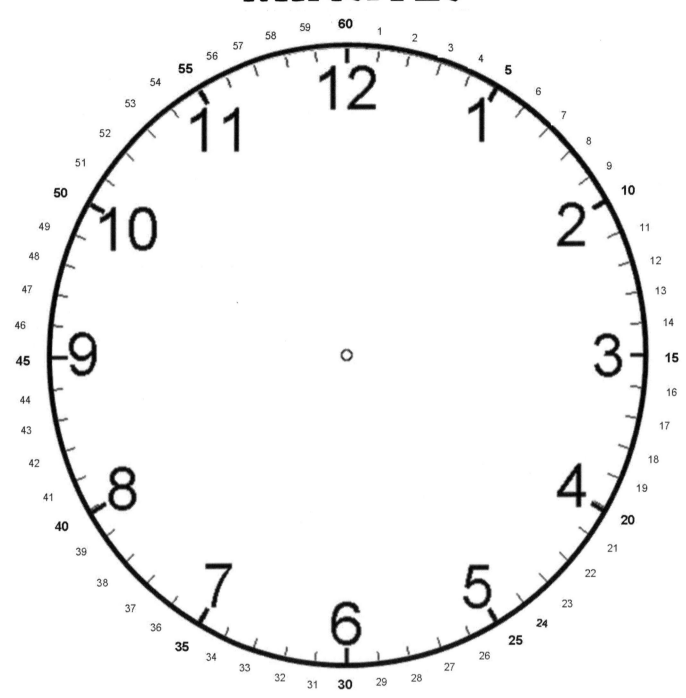

Part 2

Locate the minutes on the clock. Count each minute with your mtoto (child).

The minutes are represented by the small minute marks and clock numbers. Every clock number represents a five-minute increment and increases by 5 minutes at every clock number. For example, the clock number 1 represents 5 minutes, the clock number 2 represents 10 minutes, the clock number 3 represents 15 minutes and it continues to increase by 5 minutes at every clock number.

13

HOUR HAND

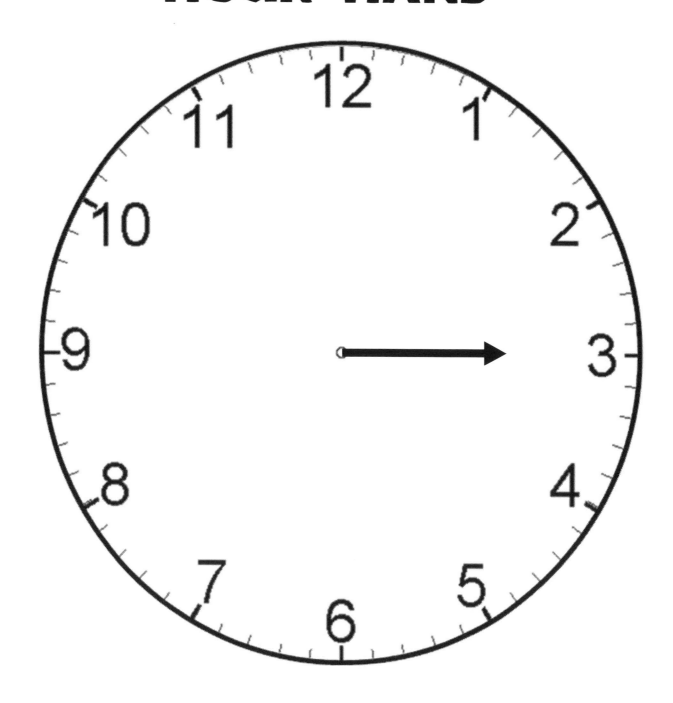

Part 2
Locate the hour hand (short hand) on the clock.

MINUTE HAND

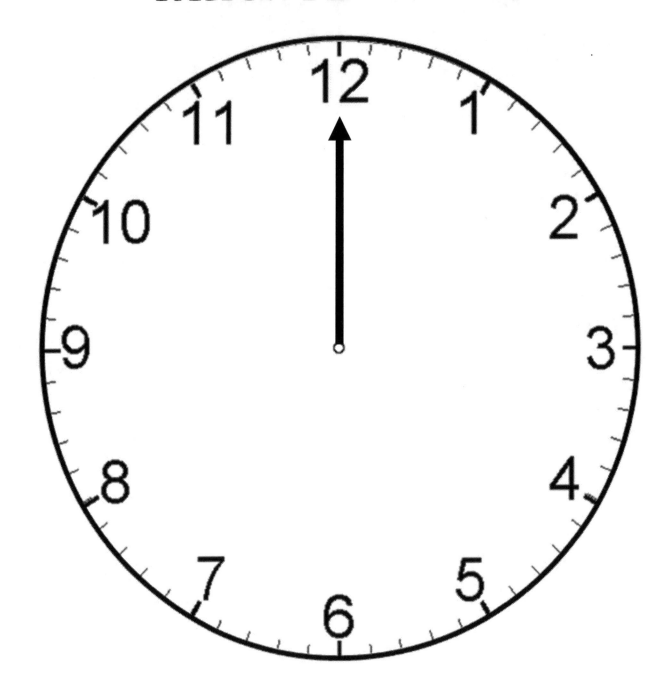

Part 2
Locate the minute hand (long hand) on the clock.

READING AN ANALOG CLOCK

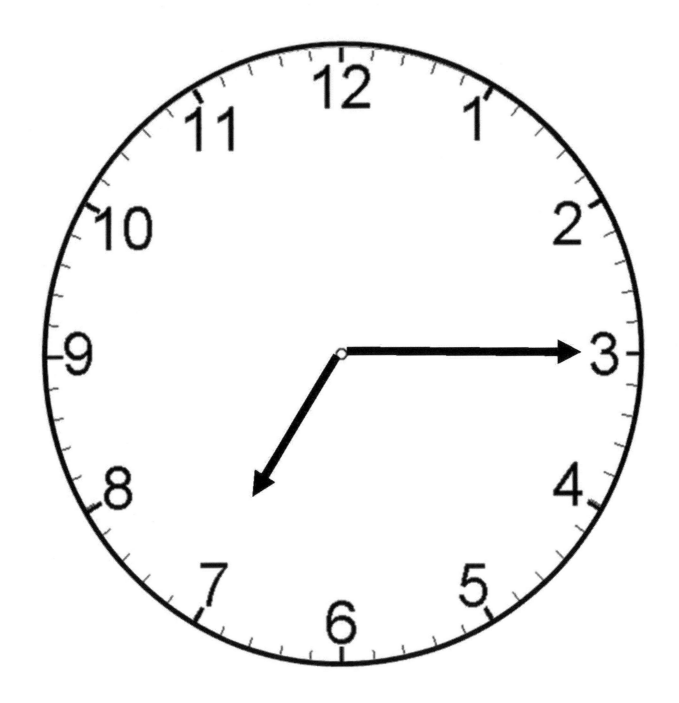

Step 1
Locate the hour hand (short hand) and identify what clock number the hand is pointing to. This is the hour.

Step 2
Locate the minute hand (long hand) and identify what minute mark or clock number the hand is pointing to. This is the minute.

What time does the clock read? _____. Mama, Baba and/or Mpendwa (Loved one), please help your mtoto (child) read the clock correctly.

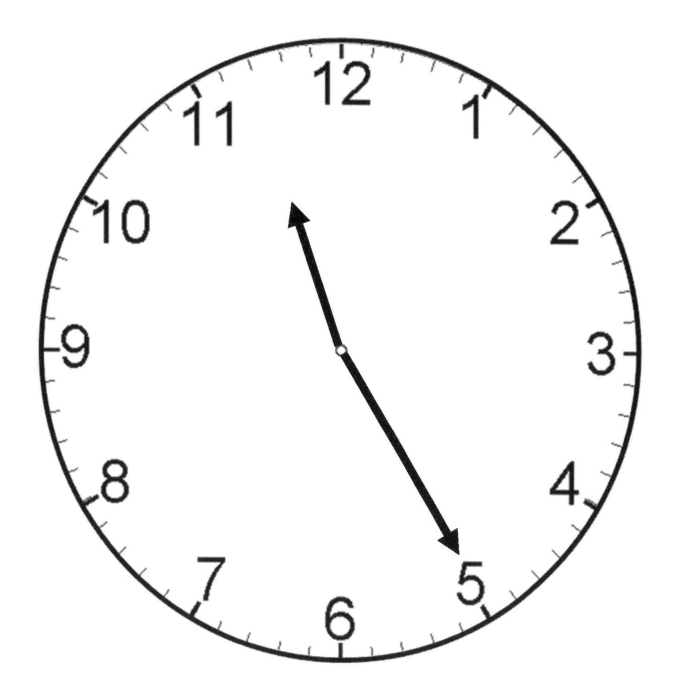

Step 1
Locate the hour hand (short hand) and identify what clock number the hand is pointing to. This is the hour.

Step 2
Locate the minute hand (long hand) and identify what minute mark or clock number the hand is pointing to. This is the minute.

What time does the clock read? _____. Mama, Baba and/or Mpendwa (Loved one), please help your mtoto (child) read the clock correctly.

There are times when the hour hand will not point directly at the clock number. To understand how to read the hour, you will determine which clock number to the left was passed last by the hour hand. For example, if the hour hand is halfway between the clock numbers 4 and 5, the hour would be 4 because it was the last number the hour hand passed. The hour is determined based on the clock number to the left that was passed last. Even in cases where the hour hand may be closer to the clock number 5, the hour is 4 until the hour hand reaches or passes the clock number 5.

The time on the analog clock below is 4:30. You will notice that the hour hand (short hand) is pointing halfway between the 4 and 5.

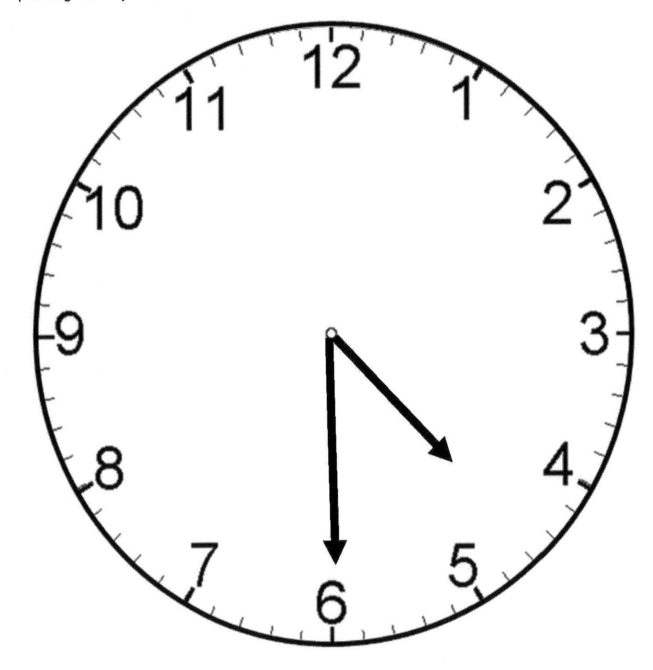

To determine the minute, you can count each minute mark and clock number or you can count the minutes by 5s using the clock numbers. If the time is 4:10, then you can count each minute mark and clock number on the analog clock until you get to 10 minutes. Or, you can count by 5s using the clock numbers. For example, clock number 1 equals 5 minutes and clock number 2 equals 10 minutes.

The time on the analog clock below is 4:10. You will notice that the minute hand (long hand) is pointing to clock number 2 which represents 10 minutes.

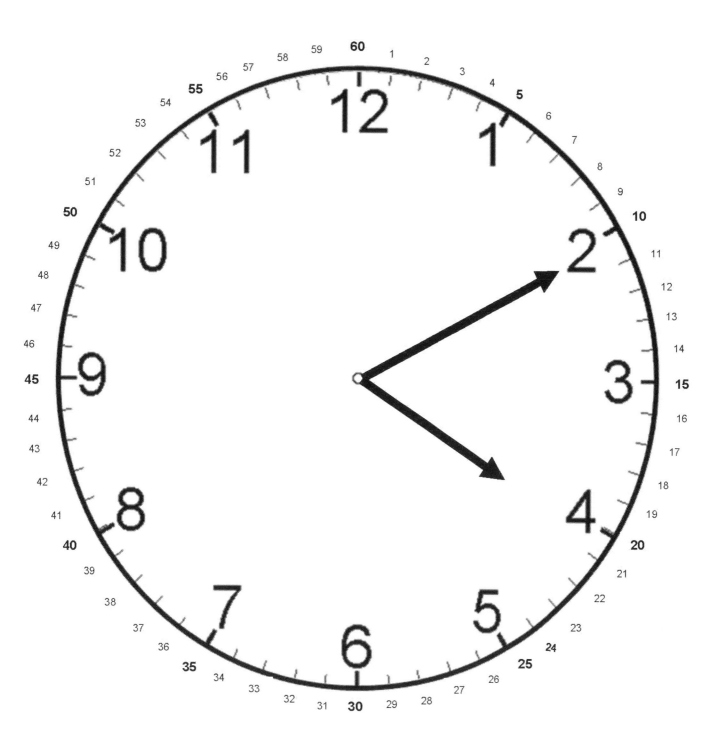

NOW, LET'S TELL TIME AND COLOR!

Color the time cover pages with Benjamin Banneker and Sekou

Don't forget to count Sekou's and Benjamin Banneker's fingers along the way!

Reading an analog clock takes practice, and the more you practice, the better you will get at understanding the concept of time!

1 O'Clock

Directions: Write the clock time on the line underneath the clock.

Directions: Draw the hour hand and minute hand for the clock time on the line.

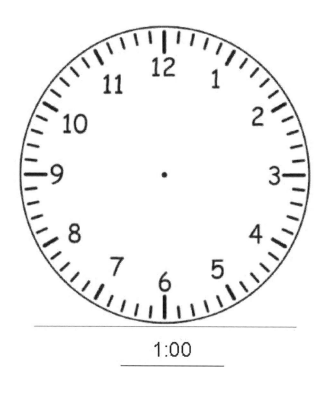

1:00

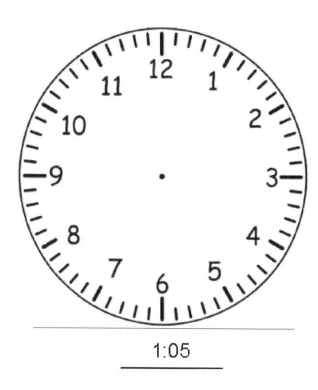

1:05

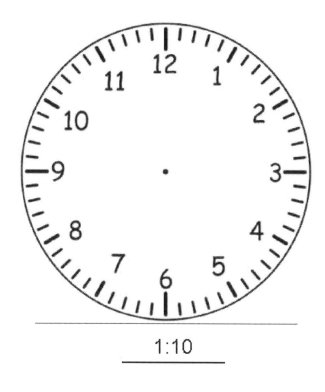

1:10

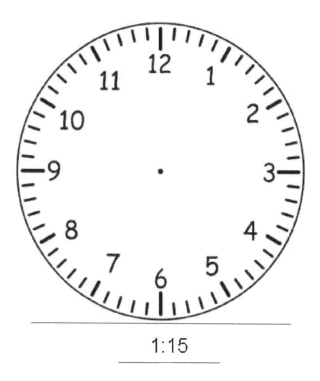

1:15

Directions: Draw the hour and minute hand for the clock time on the line.

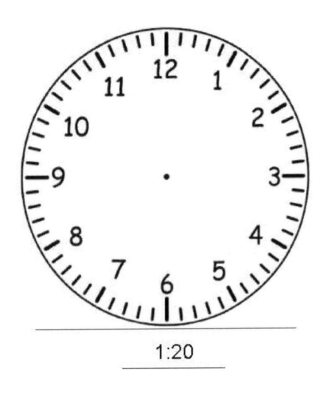

1:20

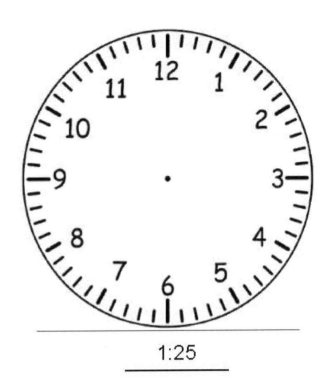

1:25

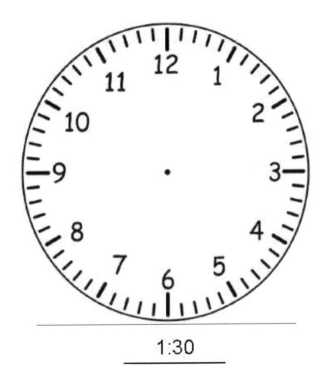

1:30

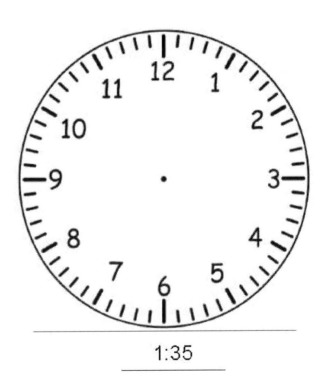

1:35

Directions: Draw the hour hand and minute hand for the clock on the line.

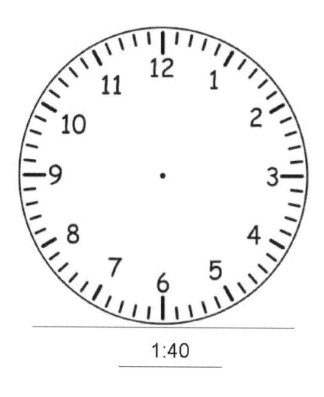

1:40

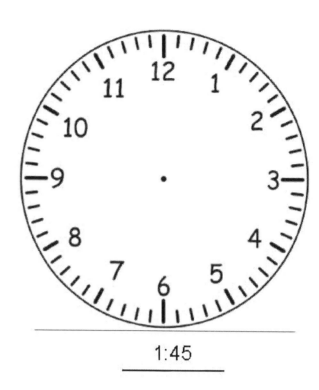

1:45

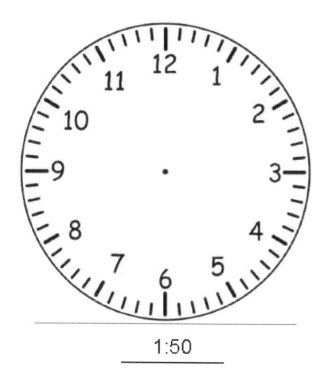

1:50

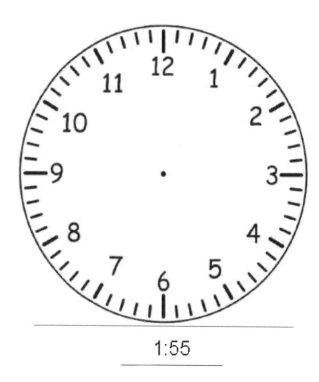

1:55

Directions: Create your own time for 1:00. Write the clock time on the line underneath the clock and then draw the hour hand and minute hand for the time you created.

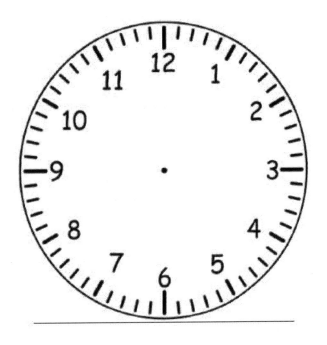

_____

_____

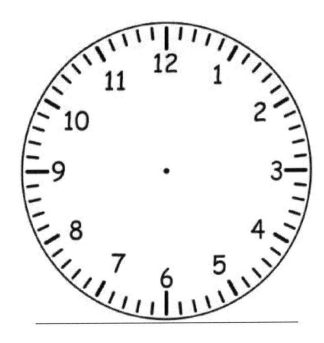

_____

_____

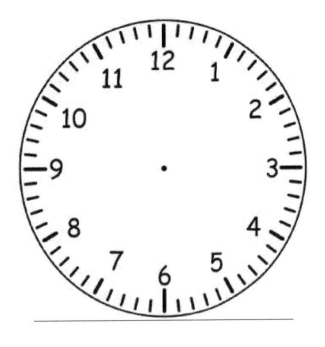

_____

_____

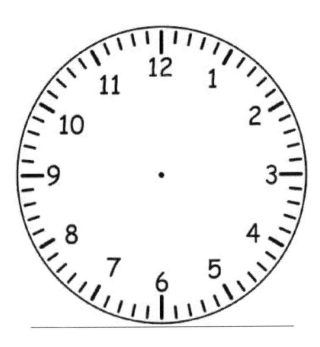

_____

_____

2 O'Clock

Directions: Write the clock time on the line underneath the clock.

Directions: Draw the hour hand and minute hand for the clock time on the line.

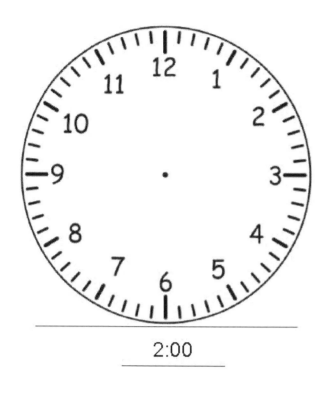

2:00

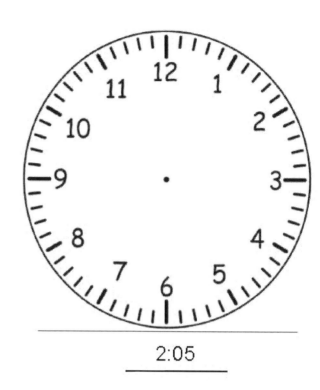

2:05

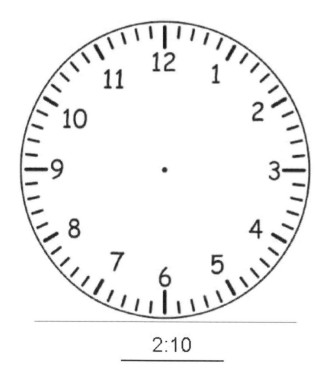

2:10

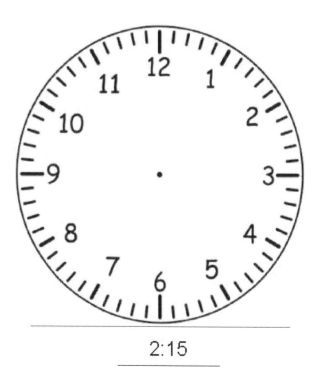

2:15

Directions: Draw the hour and minute hand for the clock time on the line.

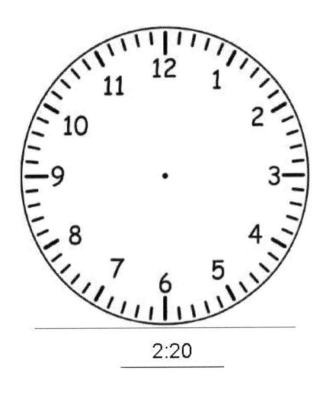

2:20

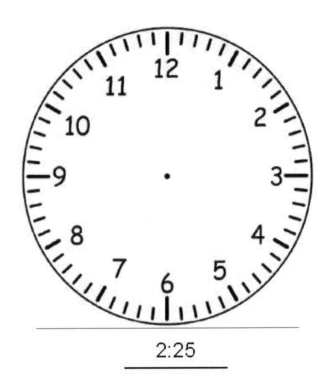

2:25

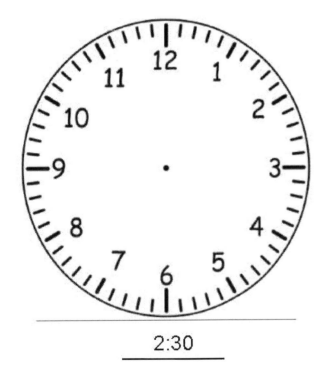

2:30

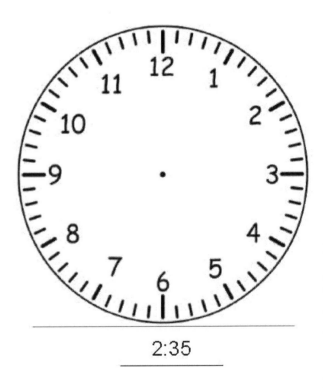

2:35

Directions: Draw the hour hand and minute hand for the clock on the line.

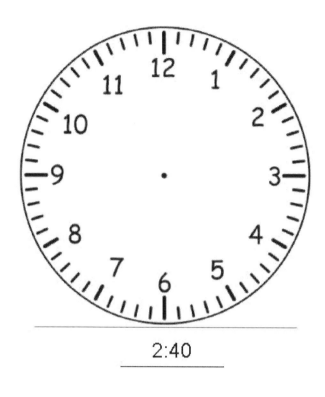

2:40

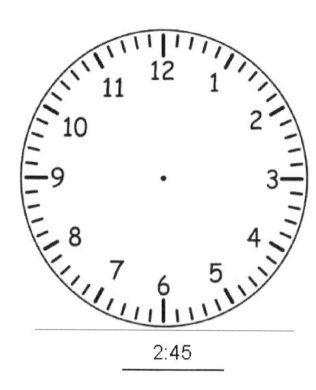

2:45

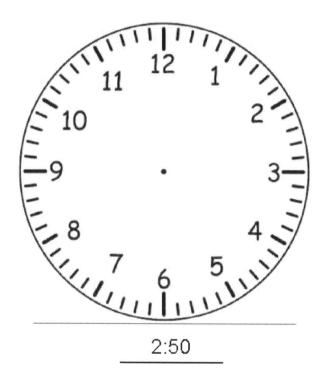

2:50

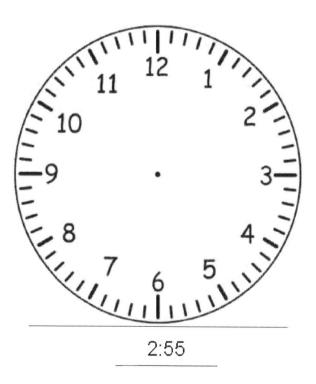

2:55

Directions: Create your own time for 2:00. Write the clock time on the line underneath the clock and then draw the hour hand and minute hand for the time you created.

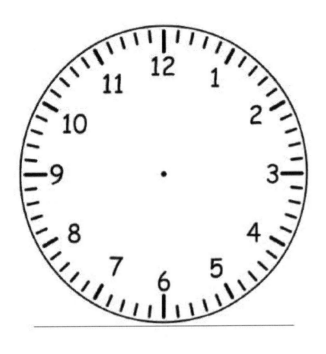

_____

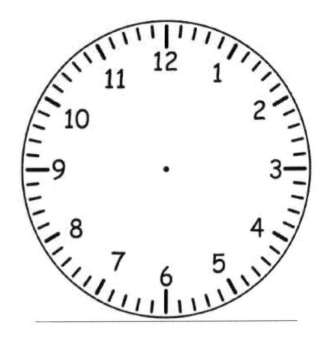

_____

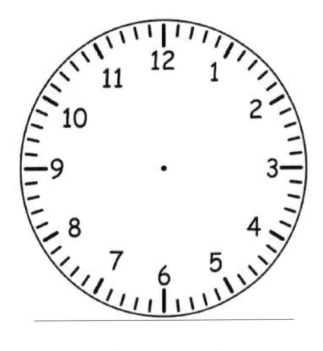

_____

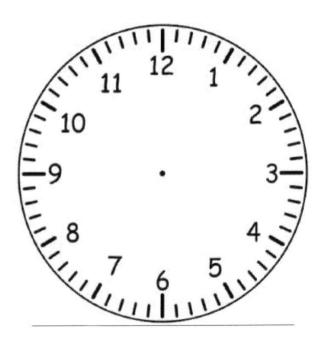

_____

3 O'Clock

Directions: Write the clock time on the line underneath the clock.

Directions: Draw the hour hand and minute hand for the clock time on the line.

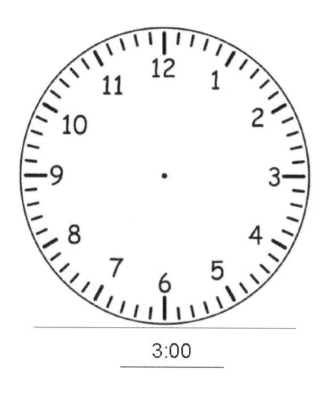

3:00

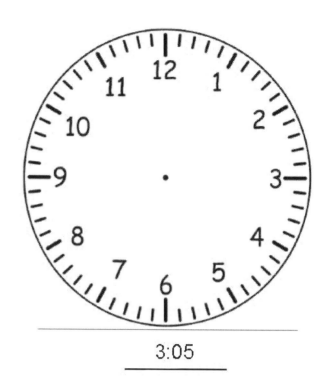

3:05

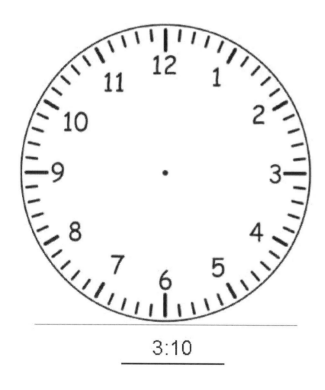

3:10

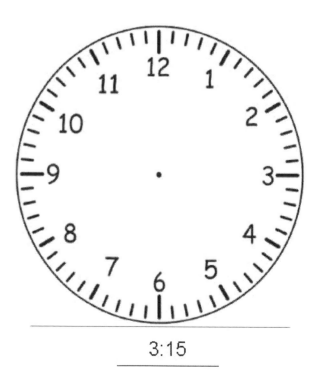

3:15

Directions: Draw the hour and minute hand for the clock time on the line.

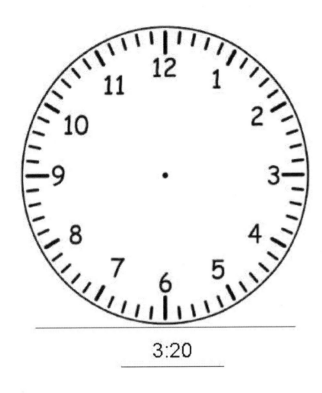

3:20

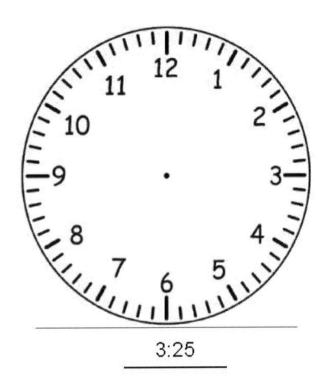

3:25

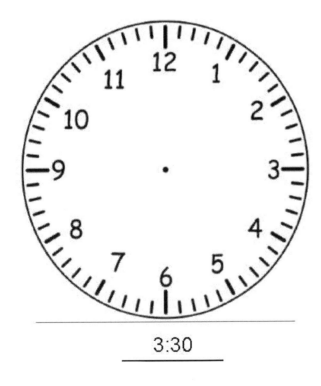

3:30

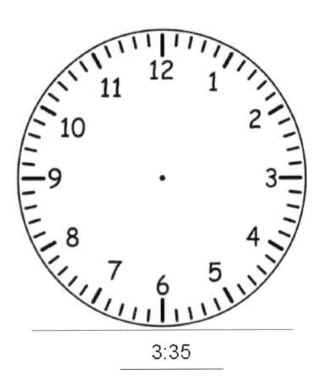

3:35

Directions: Draw the hour hand and minute hand for the clock on the line.

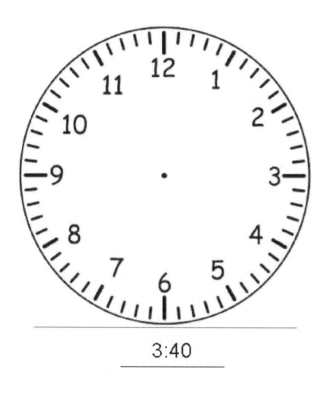

3:40

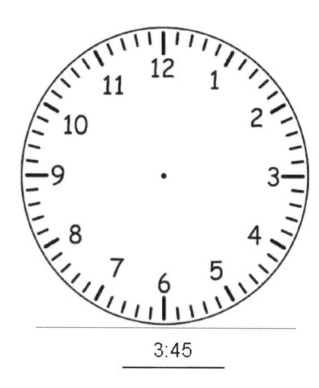

3:45

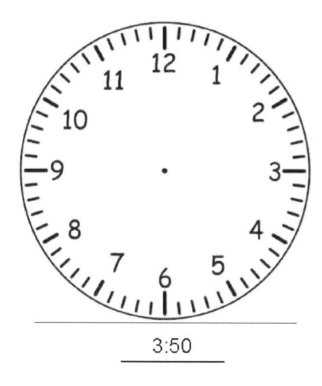

3:50

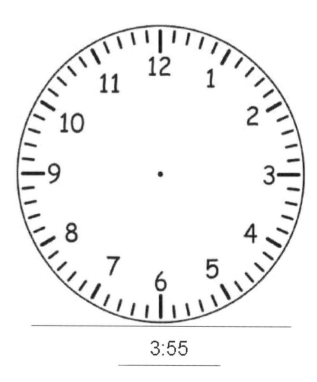

3:55

Directions: Create your own time for 3:00. Write the clock time on the line underneath the clock and then draw the hour hand and minute hand for the time you created.

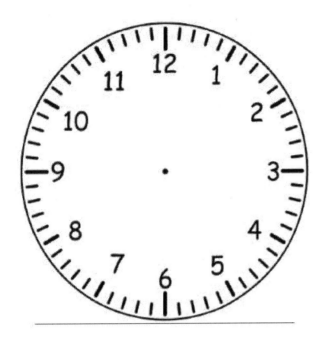

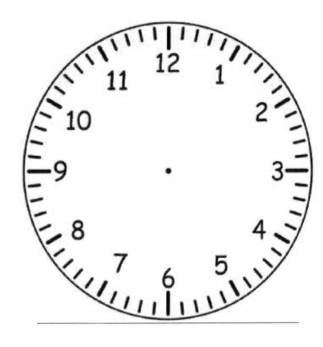

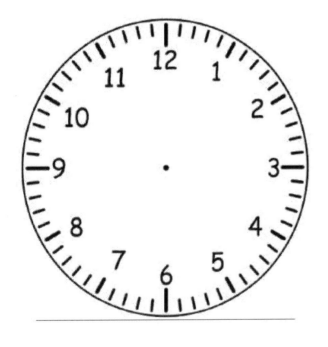

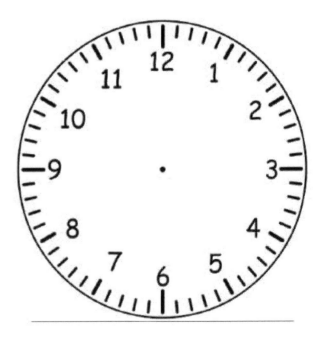

4 O'Clock

Directions: Write the clock time on the line underneath the clock.

Directions: Draw the hour hand and minute hand for the clock time on the line.

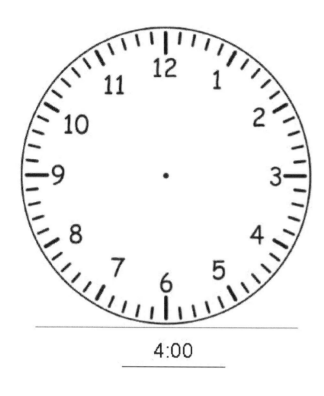

4:00

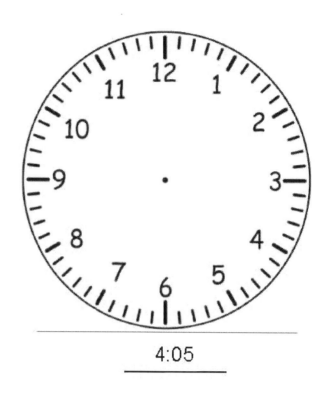

4:05

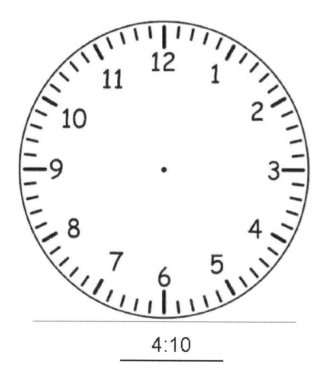

4:10

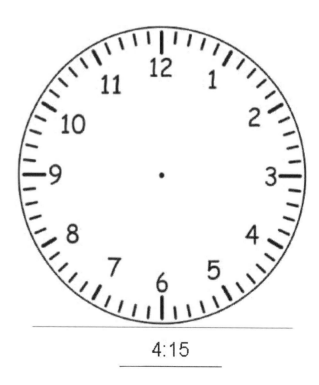

4:15

Directions: Draw the hour and minute hand for the clock time on the line.

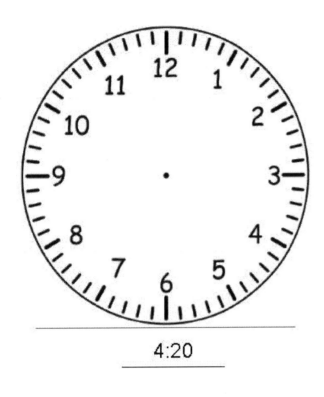

4:20

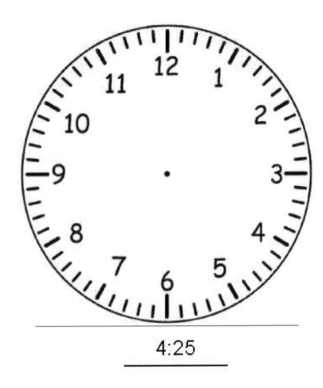

4:25

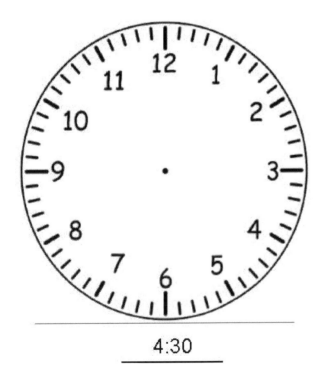

4:30

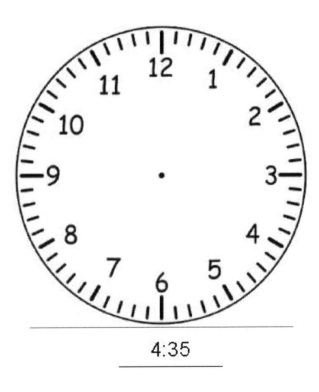

4:35

Directions: Draw the hour hand and minute hand for the clock on the line.

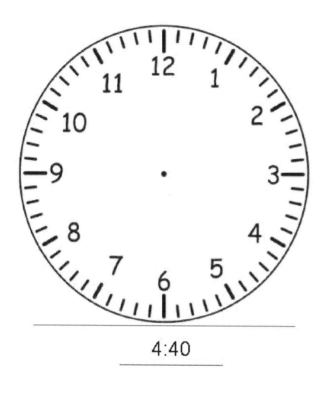

4:40

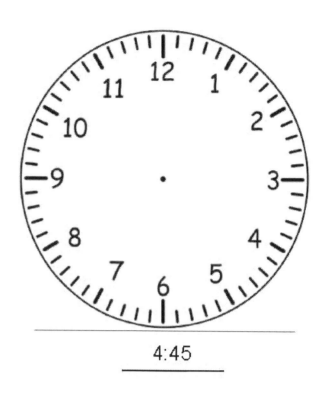

4:45

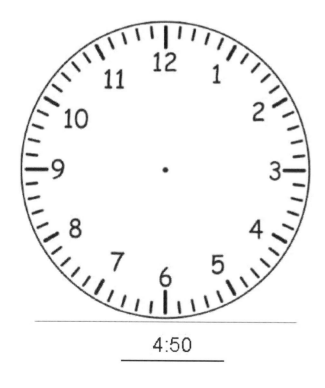

4:50

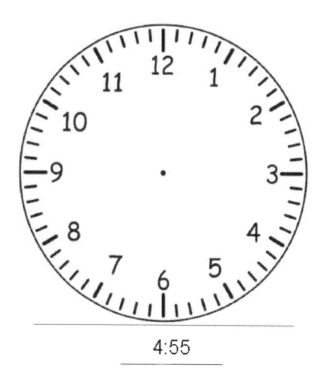

4:55

Directions: Create your own time for 4:00. Write the clock time on the line underneath the clock and then draw the hour hand and minute hand for the time you created.

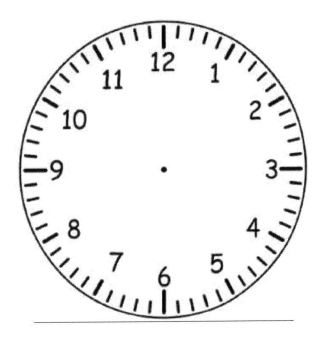

_____

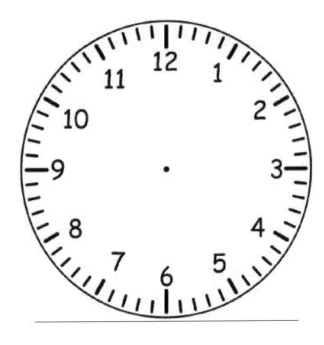

_____

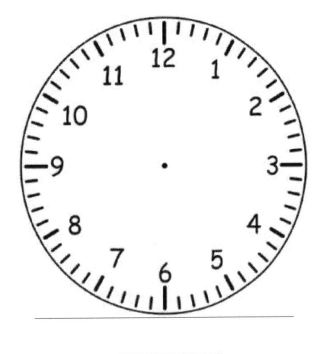

_____

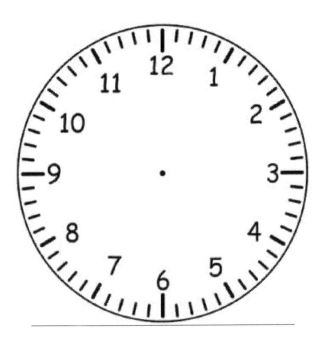

_____

5 O'Clock

Directions: Write the clock time on the line underneath the clock.

Directions: Draw the hour hand and minute hand for the clock time on the line.

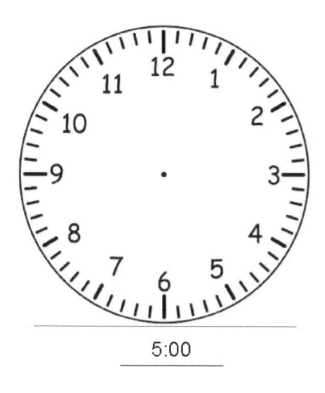

5:00

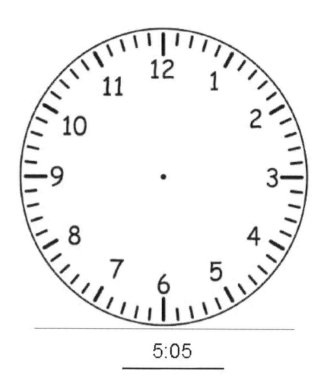

5:05

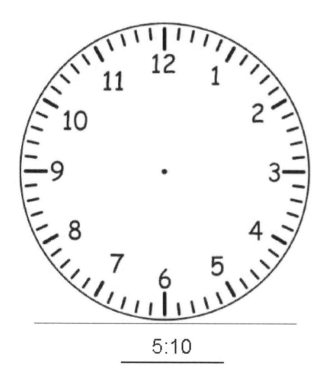

5:10

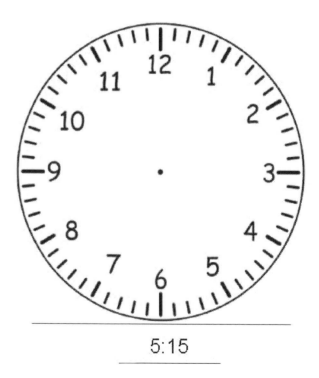

5:15

Directions: Draw the hour and minute hand for the clock time on the line.

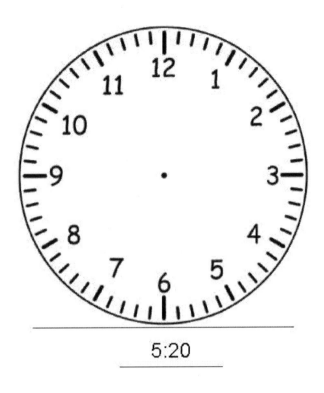

5:20

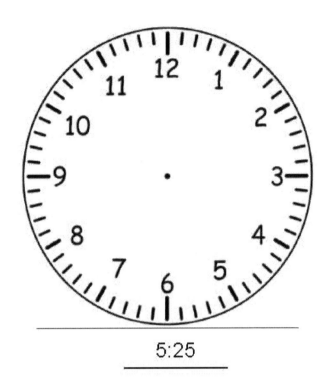

5:25

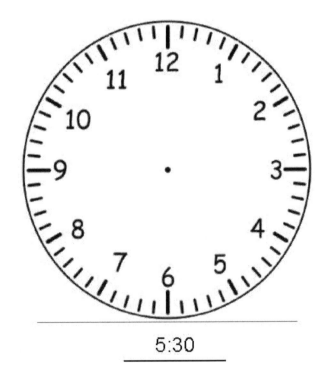

5:30

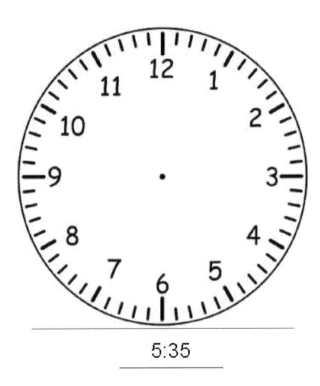

5:35

Directions: Draw the hour hand and minute hand for the clock on the line.

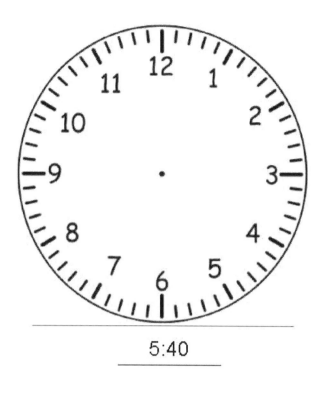

5:40

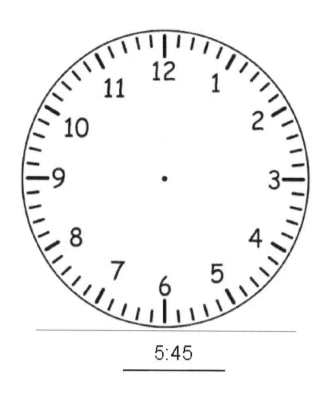

5:45

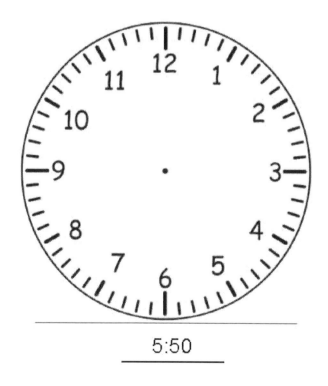

5:50

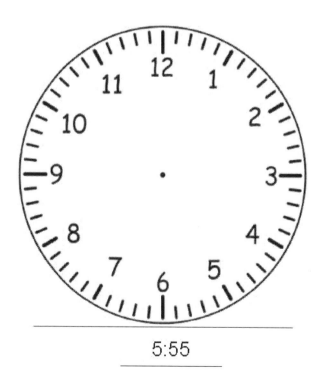

5:55

Directions: Create your own time for 5:00. Write the clock time on the line underneath the clock and then draw the hour hand and minute hand for the time you created.

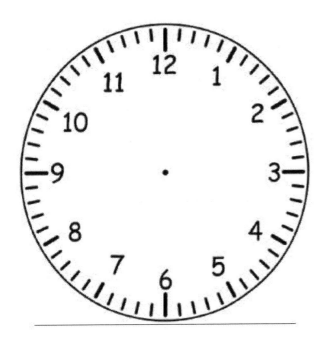

_____

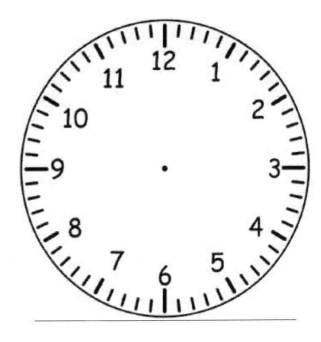

_____

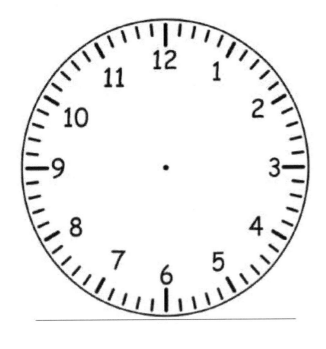

_____

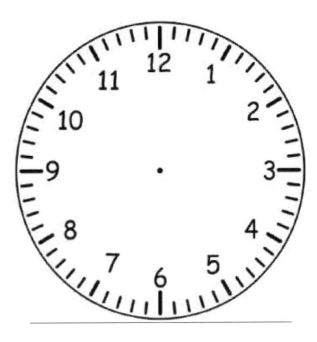

_____

6 O'Clock

Directions: Write the clock time on the line underneath the clock.

Directions: Draw the hour hand and minute hand for the clock time on the line.

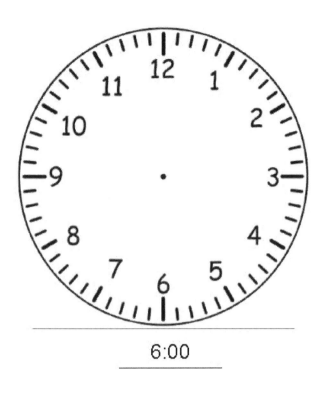

6:00

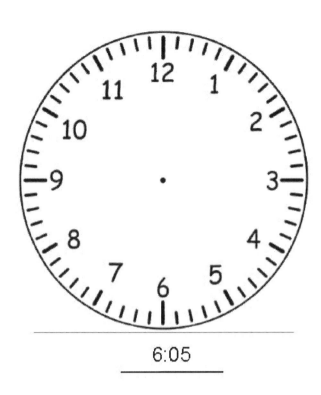

6:05

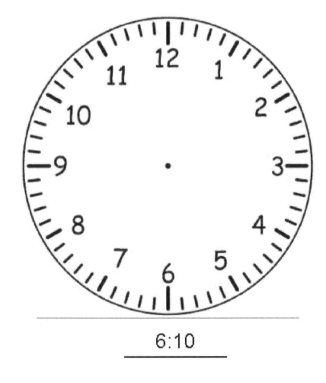

6:10

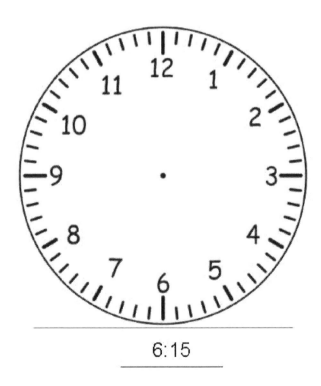

6:15

Directions: Draw the hour and minute hand for the clock time on the line.

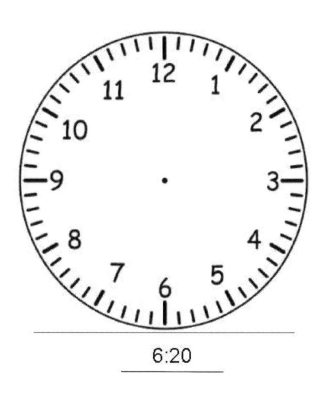

6:20

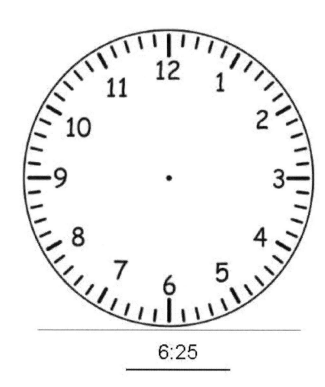

6:25

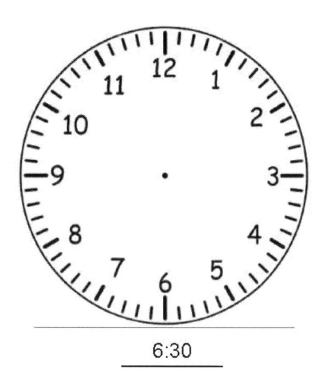

6:30

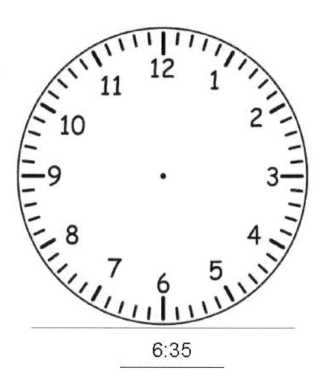

6:35

Directions: Draw the hour hand and minute hand for the clock on the line.

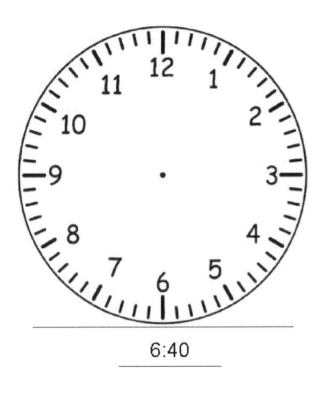

6:40

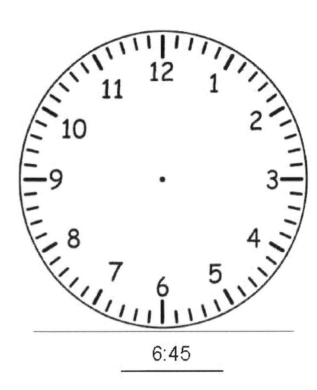

6:45

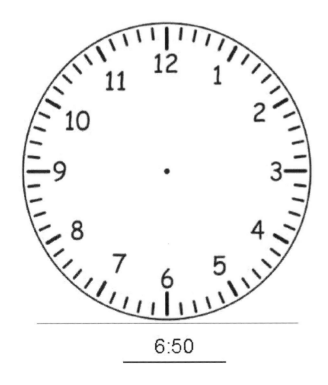

6:50

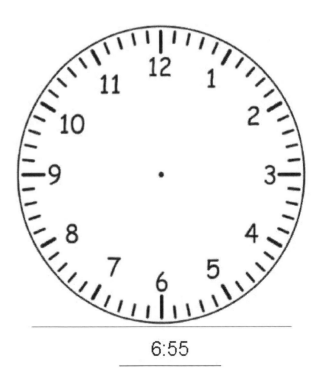

6:55

56

Directions: Create your own time for 6:00. Write the clock time on the line underneath the clock and then draw the hour hand and minute hand for the time you created.

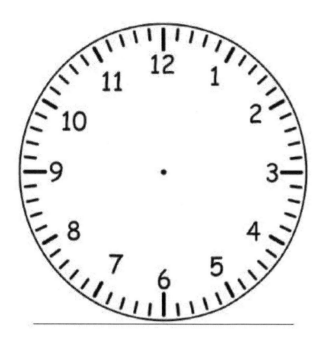

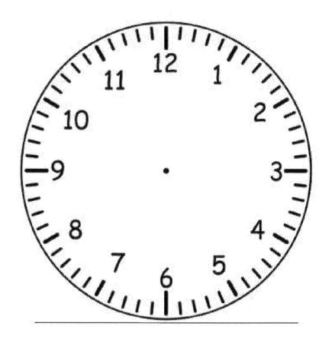

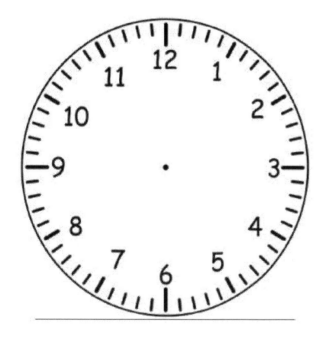

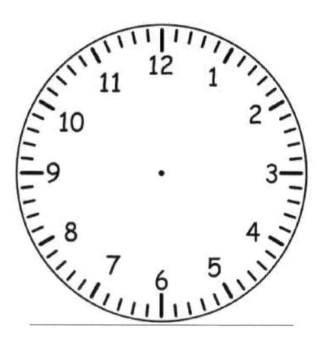

7 O'Clock

Directions: Write the clock time on the line underneath the clock.

Directions: Draw the hour hand and minute hand for the clock time on the line.

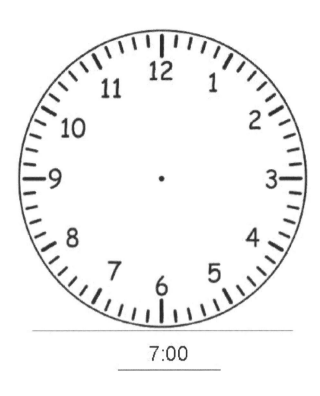

7:00

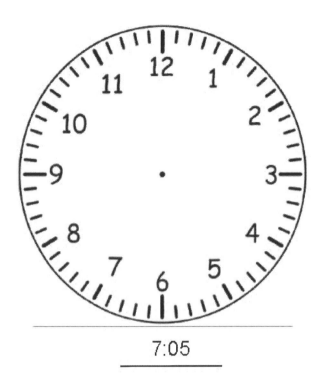

7:05

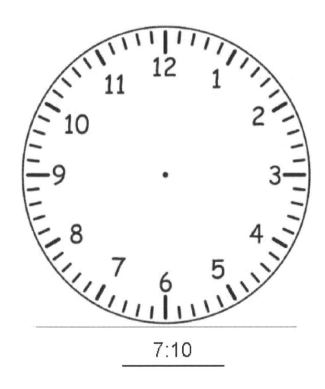

7:10

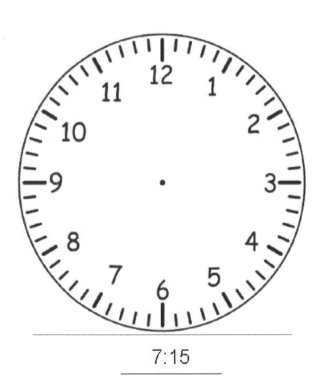

7:15

Directions: Draw the hour and minute hand for the clock time on the line.

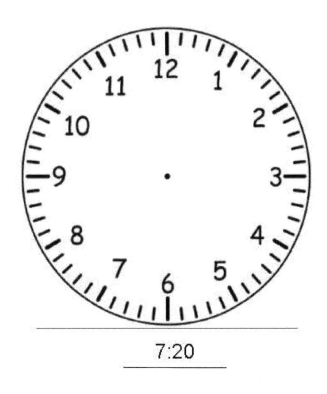

7:20

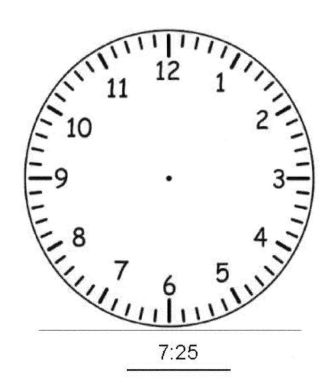

7:25

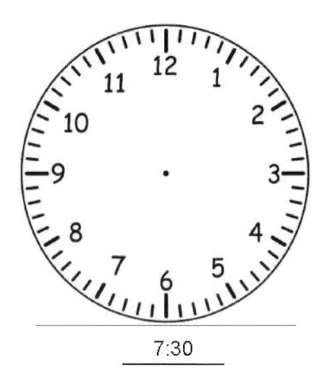

7:30

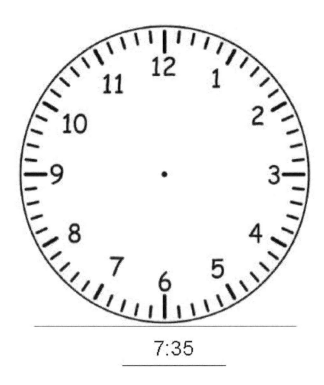

7:35

Directions: Draw the hour hand and minute hand for the clock on the line.

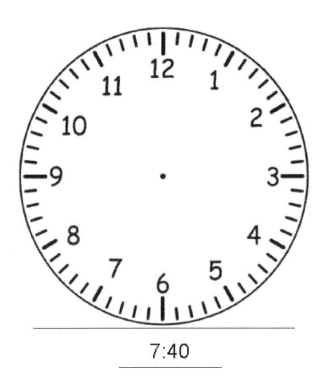

7:40

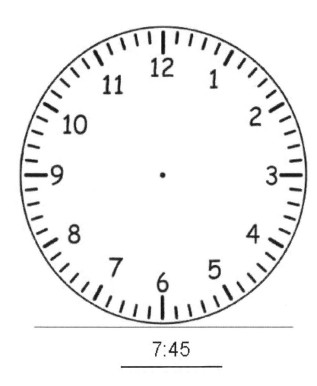

7:45

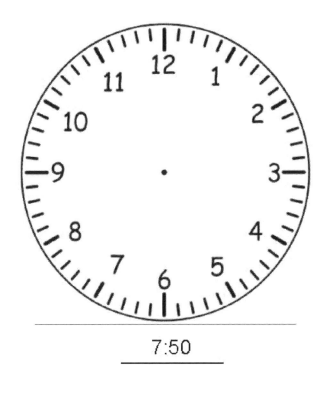

7:50

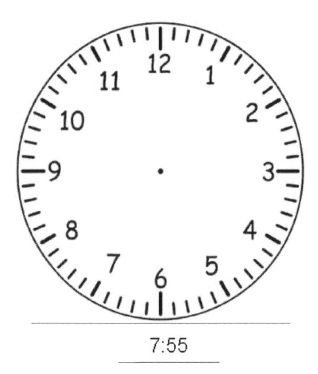

7:55

Directions: Create your own time for 7:00. Write the clock time on the line underneath the clock and then draw the hour hand and minute hand for the time you created.

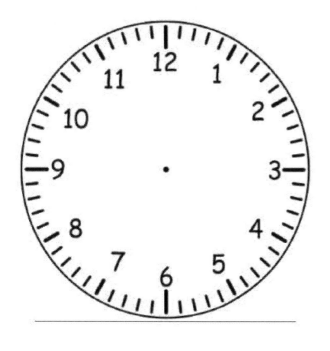

_____

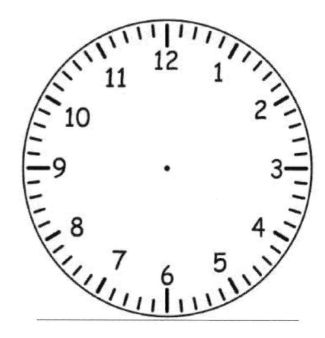

_____

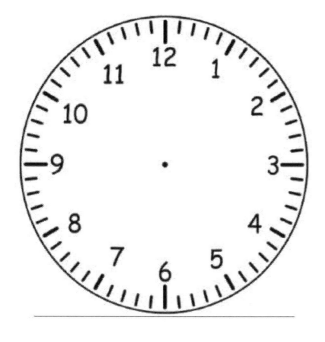

_____

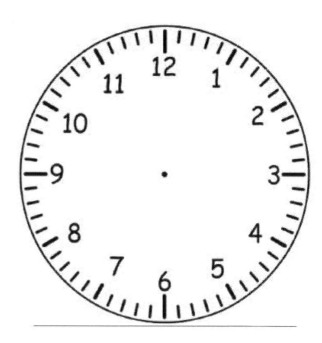

_____

8 O'Clock

Directions: Write the clock time on the line underneath the clock.

Directions: Draw the hour hand and minute hand for the clock time on the line.

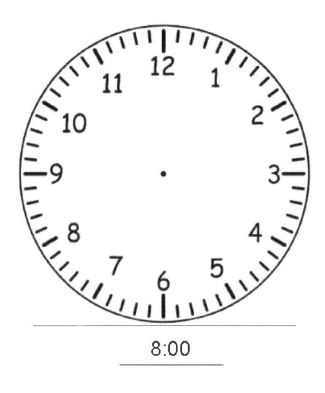

8:00

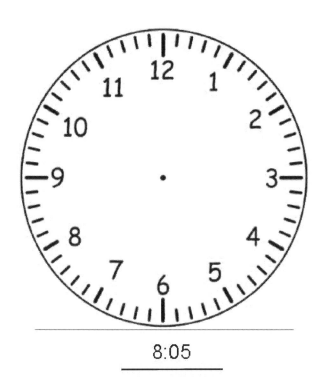

8:05

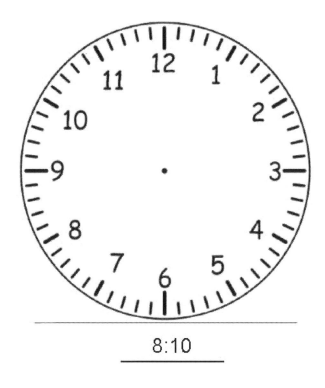

8:10

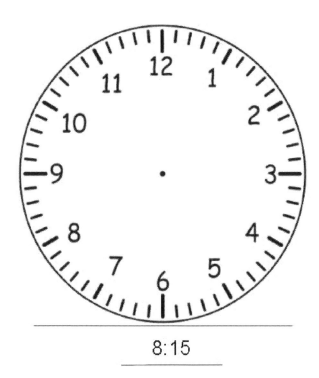

8:15

Directions: Draw the hour and minute hand for the clock time on the line.

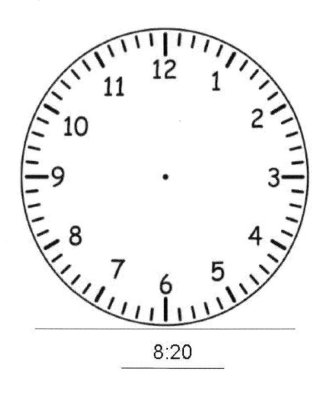

8:20

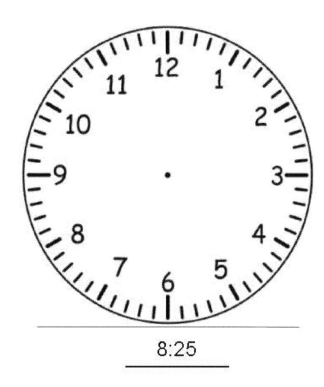

8:25

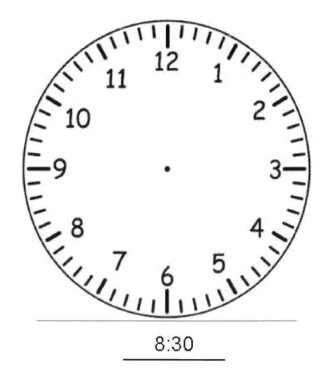

8:30

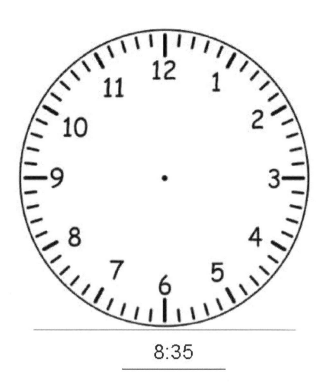

8:35

Directions: Draw the hour hand and minute hand for the clock on the line.

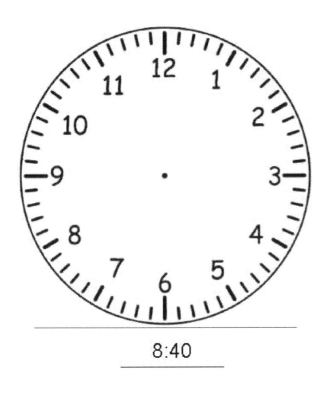

8:40

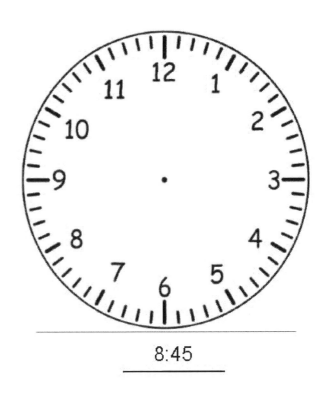

8:45

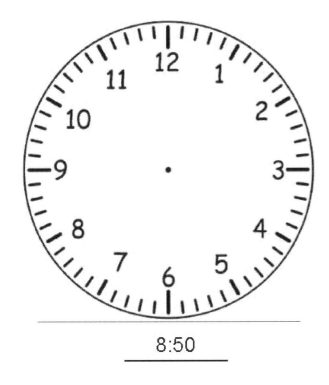

8:50

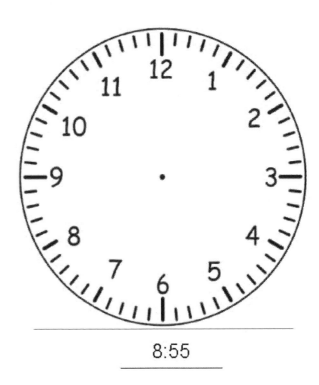

8:55

Directions: Create your own time for 8:00. Write the clock time on the line underneath the clock and then draw the hour hand and minute hand for the time you created.

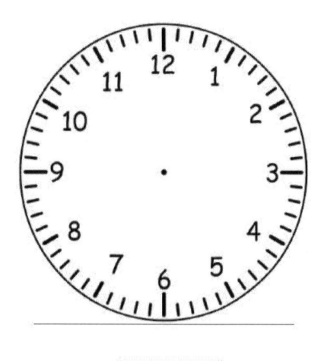

_____

_____

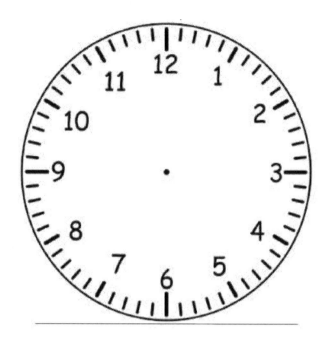

_____

_____

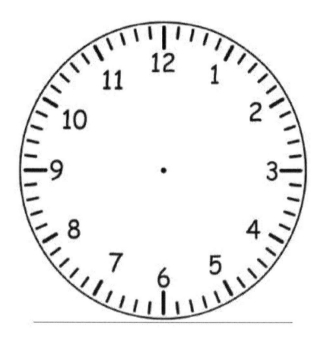

_____

_____

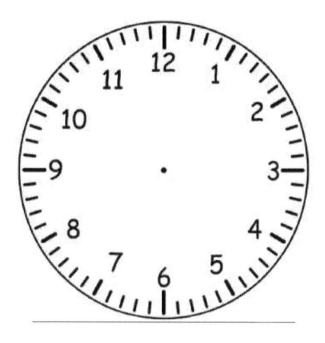

_____

_____

9 O'Clock

Directions: Write the clock time on the line underneath the clock.

_____   _____   _____

_____   _____   _____

_____   _____   _____

_____   _____   _____

71

Directions: Draw the hour hand and minute hand for the clock time on the line.

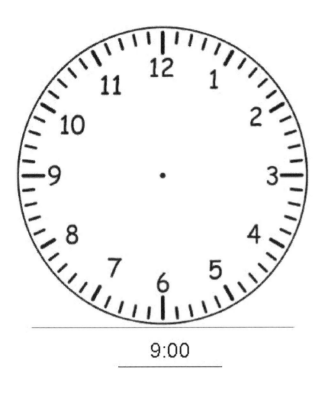

9:00
_____

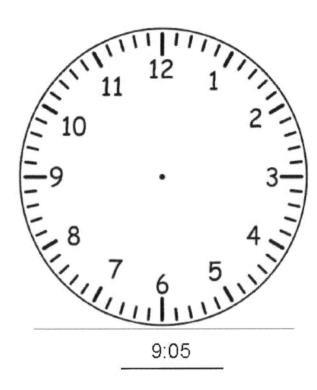

9:05
_____

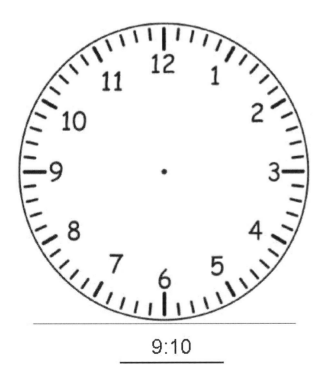

9:10
_____

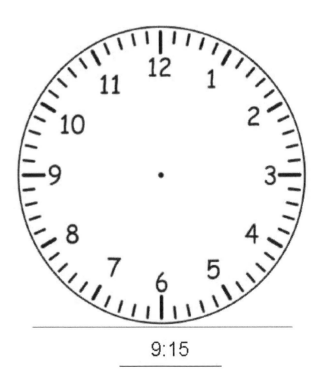

9:15
_____

Directions: Draw the hour and minute hand for the clock time on the line.

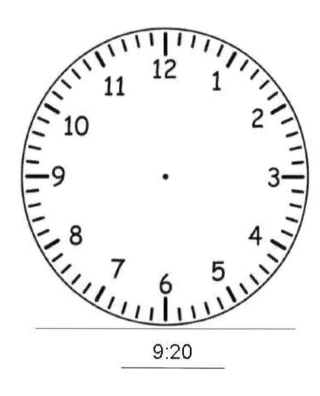

9:20

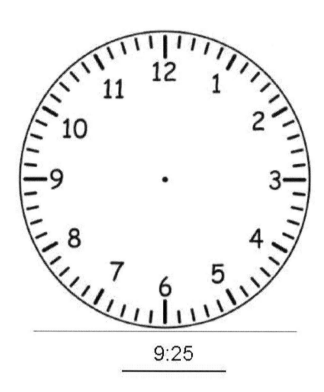

9:25

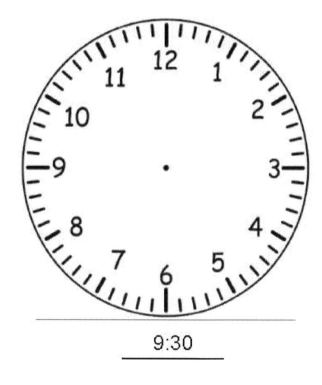

9:30

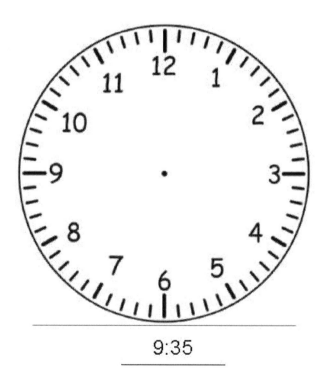

9:35

Directions: Draw the hour hand and minute hand for the clock on the line.

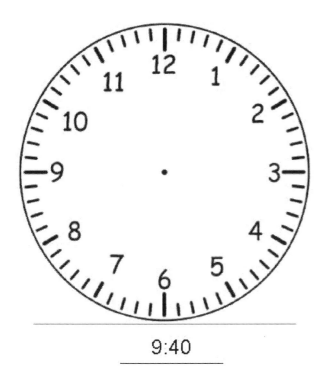

9:40

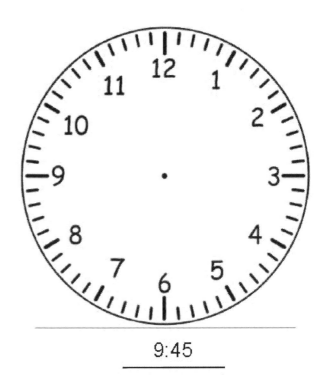

9:45

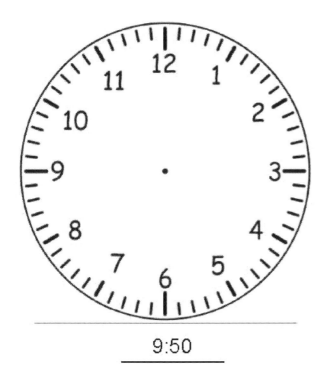

9:50

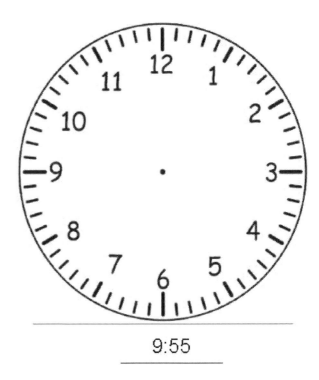

9:55

Directions: Create your own time for 9:00. Write the clock time on the line underneath the clock and then draw the hour hand and minute hand for the time you created.

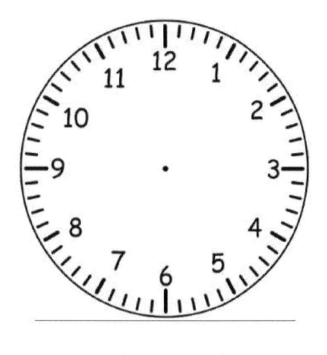

_____

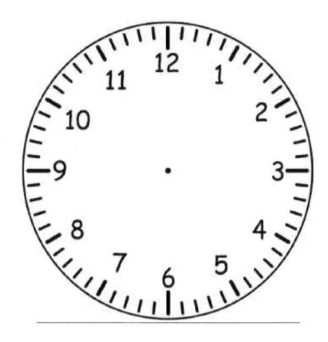

_____

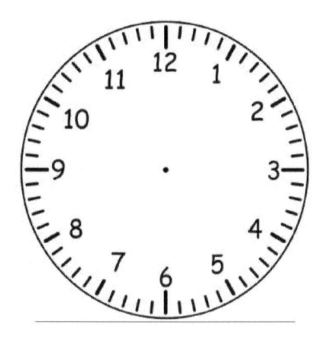

_____

_____

10 O'Clock

Directions: Write the clock time on the line underneath the clock.

Directions: Draw the hour hand and minute hand for the clock time on the line.

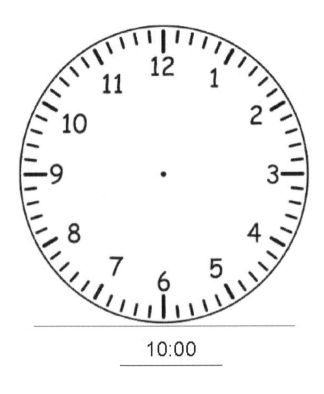

10:00

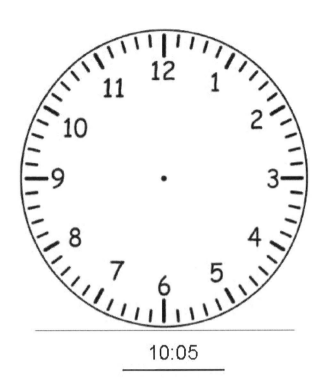

10:05

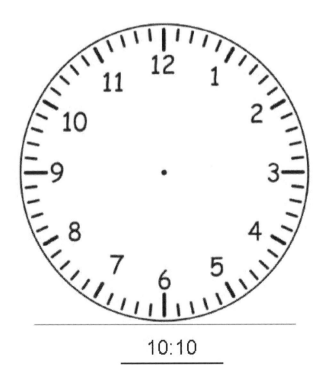

10:10

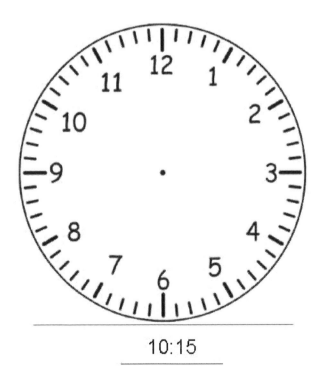

10:15

Directions: Draw the hour and minute hand for the clock time on the line.

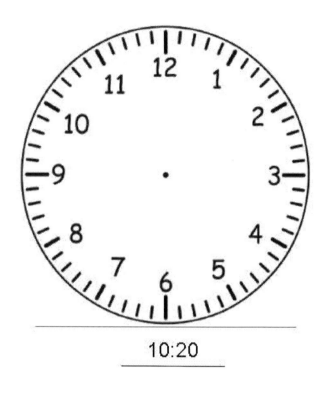

10:20

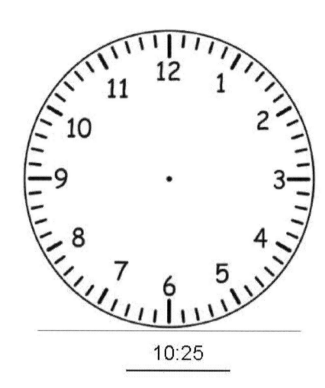

10:25

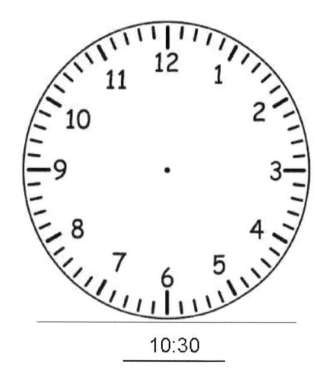

10:30

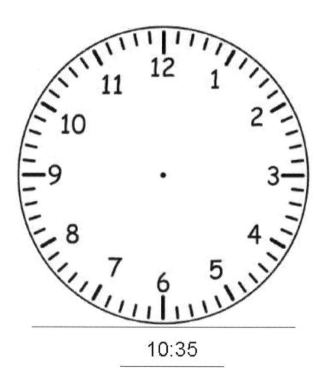

10:35

Directions: Draw the hour hand and minute hand for the clock on the line.

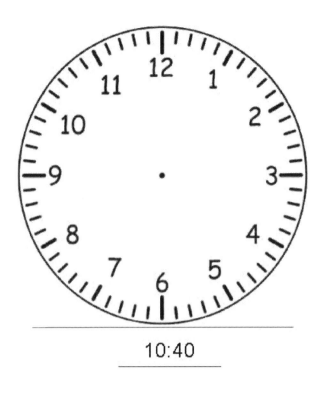

10:40

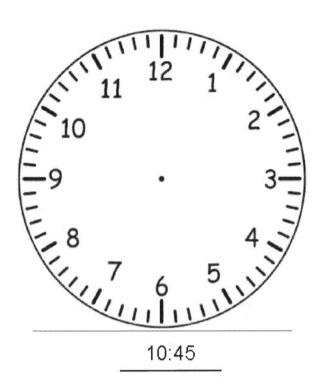

10:45

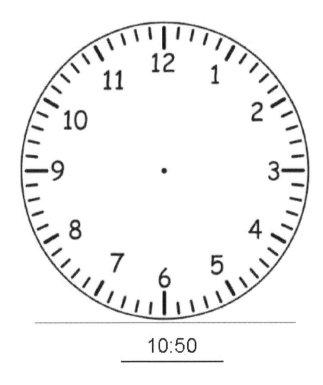

10:50

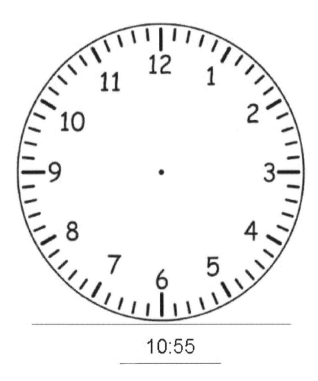

10:55

Directions: Create your own time for 10:00. Write the clock time on the line underneath the clock and then draw the hour hand and minute hand for the time you created.

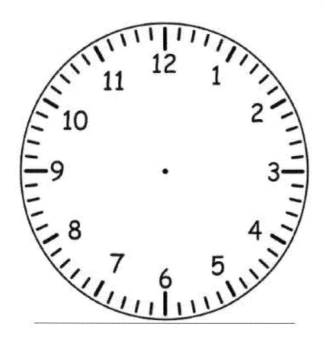

_____

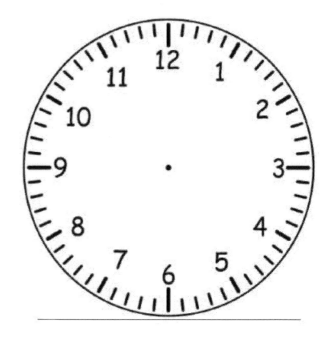

_____

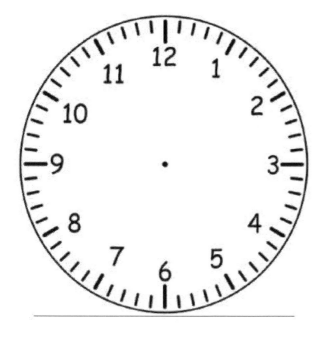

_____

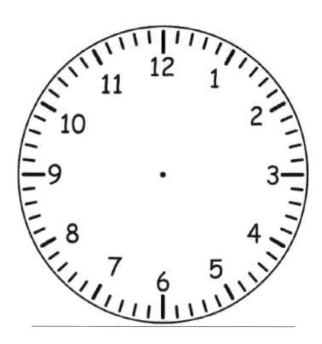

_____

11 O'Clock

Directions: Write the clock time on the line underneath the clock.

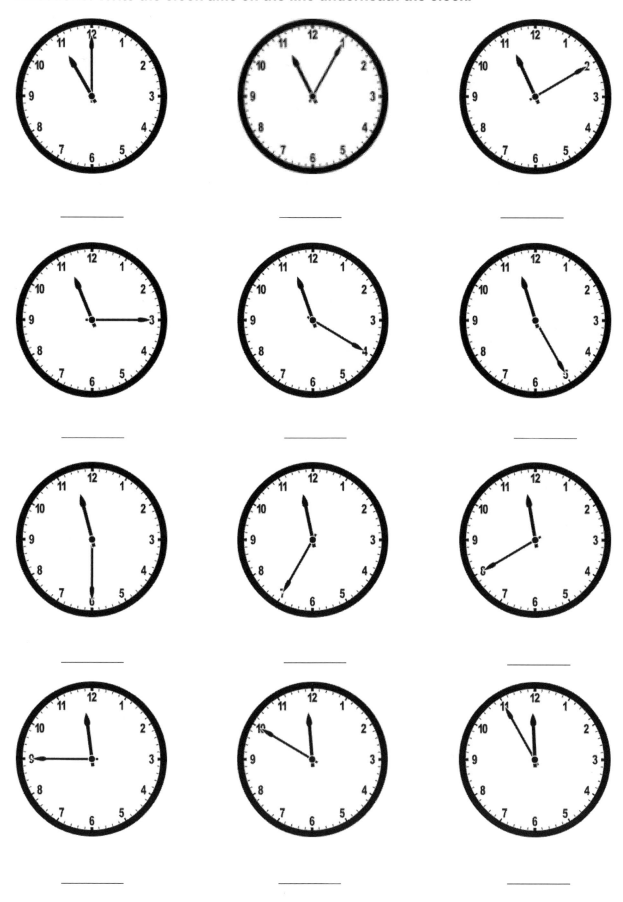

Directions: Draw the hour hand and minute hand for the clock time on the line.

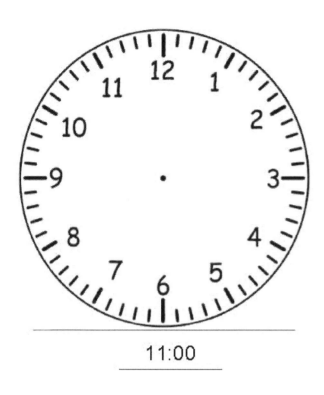

11:00

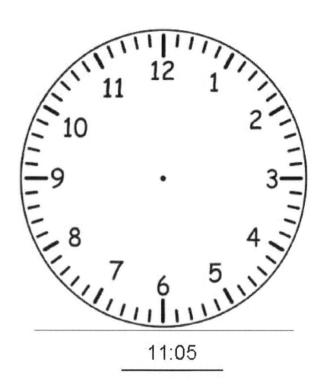

11:05

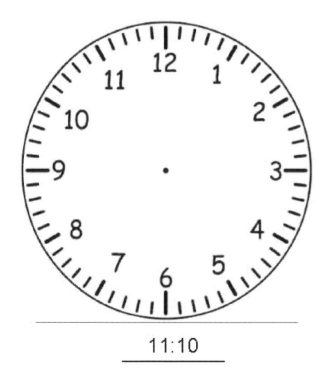

11:10

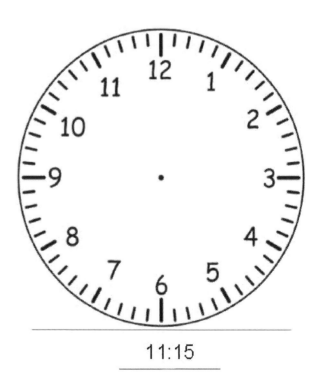

11:15

www.kujichaguliapress.com

Directions: Draw the hour and minute hand for the clock time on the line.

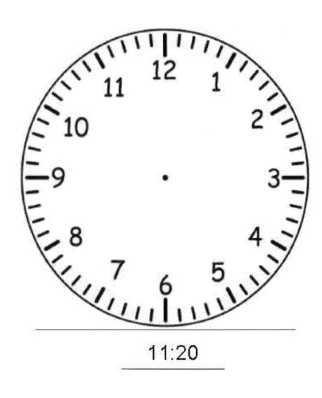

11:20

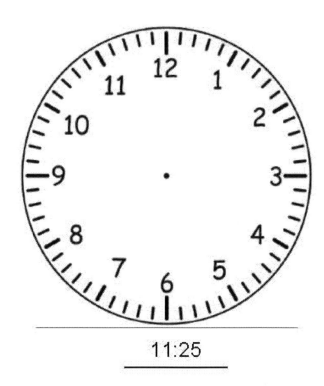

11:25

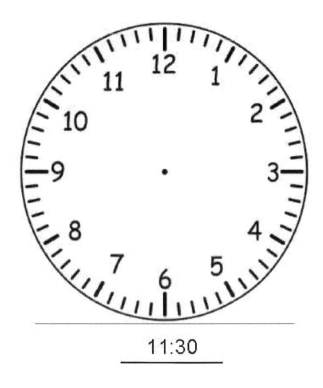

11:30

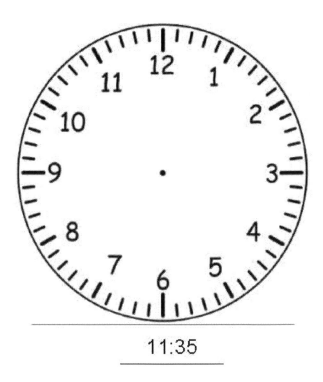

11:35

Directions: Draw the hour hand and minute hand for the clock on the line.

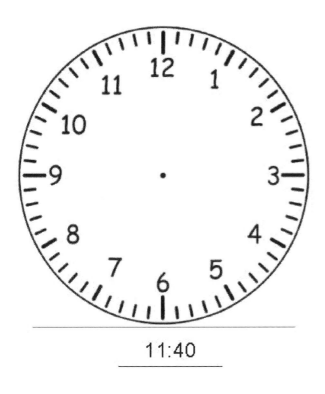

11:40

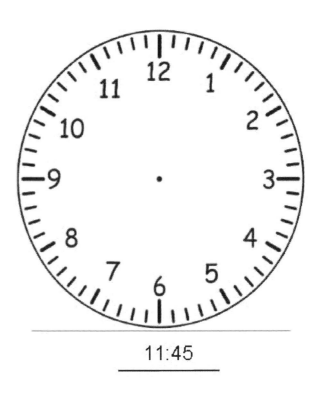

11:45

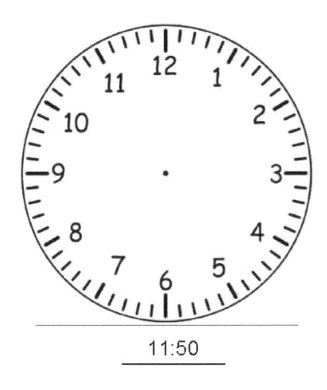

11:50

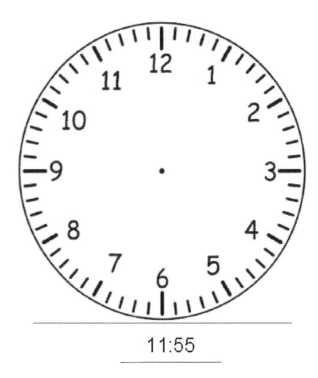

11:55

Directions: Create your own time for 11:00. Write the clock time on the line underneath the clock and then draw the hour hand and minute hand for the time you created.

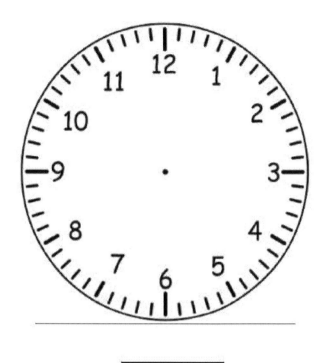

_____

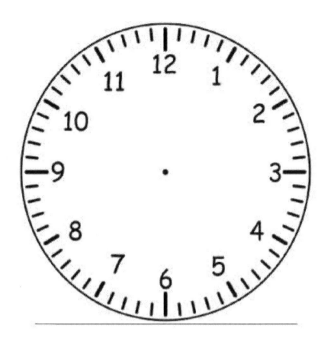

_____

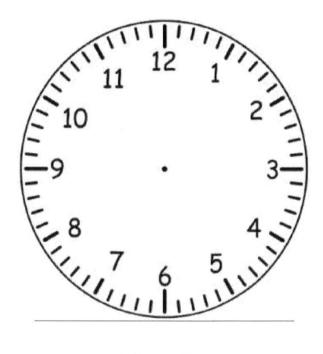

_____

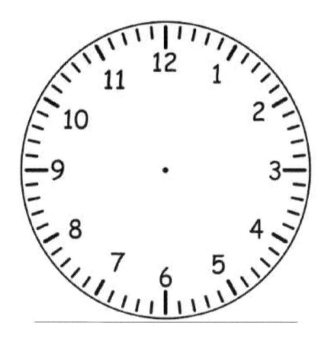

_____

12 O'Clock

Directions: Write the clock time on the line underneath the clock.

---   ---   ---

---   ---   ---

---   ---   ---

---   ---   ---

Directions: Draw the hour hand and minute hand for the clock time on the line.

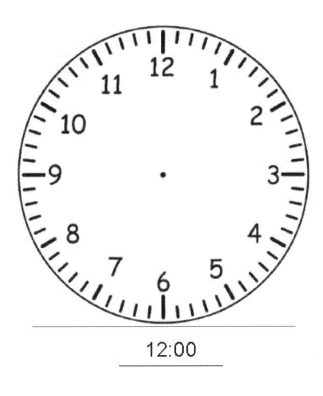

12:00

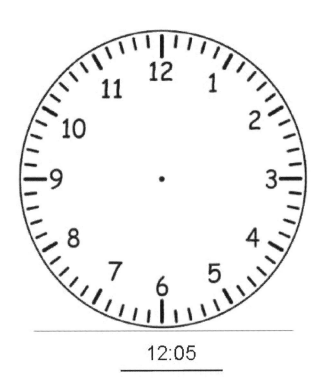

12:05

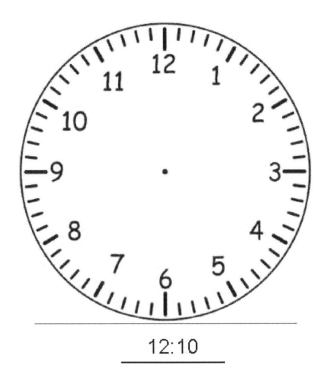

12:10

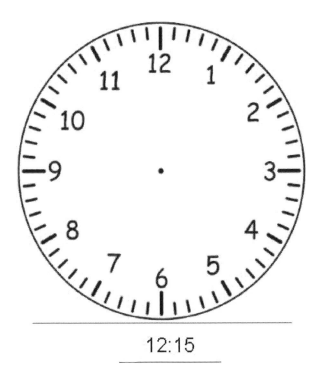

12:15

www.kujichaguliapress.com

Directions: Draw the hour and minute hand for the clock time on the line.

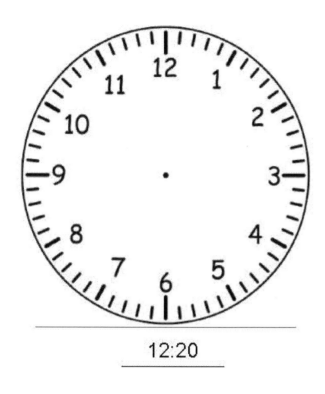

12:20
_____

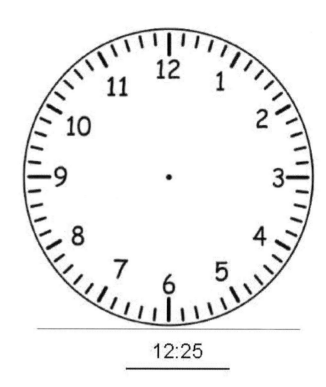

12:25
_____

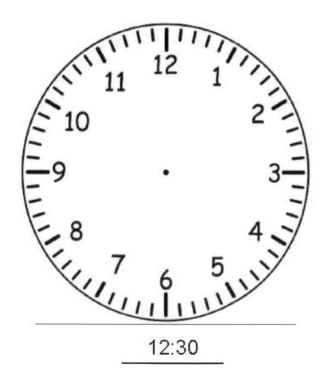

12:30
_____

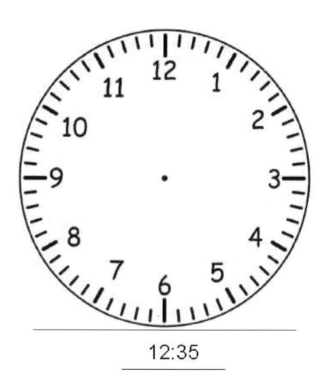

12:35
_____

Directions: Draw the hour hand and minute hand for the clock on the line.

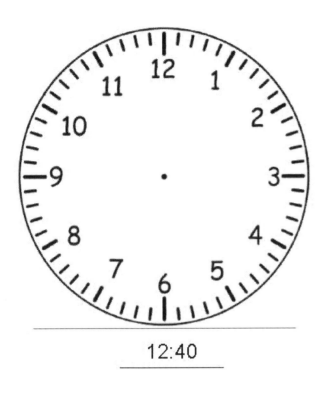

12:40

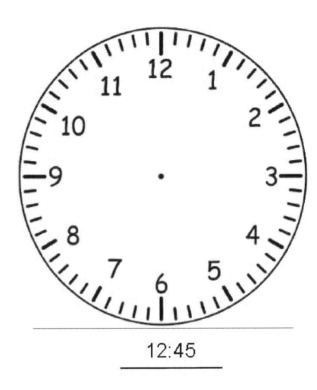

12:45

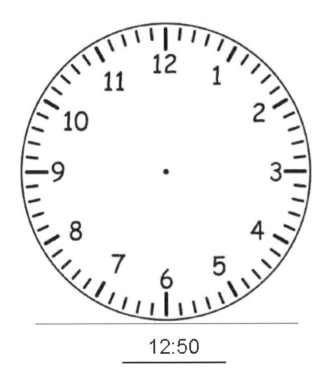

12:50

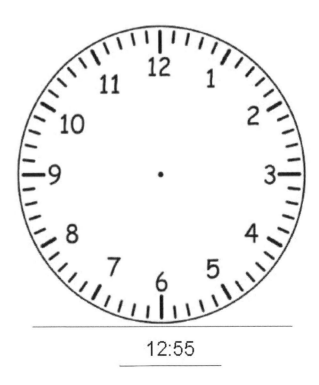

12:55

       www.kujichaguliapress.com

Directions: Create your own time for 12:00. Write the clock time on the line underneath the clock and then draw the hour hand and minute hand for the time you created.

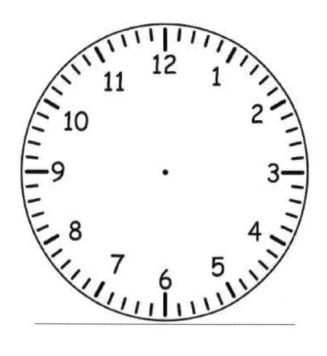

_____

_____

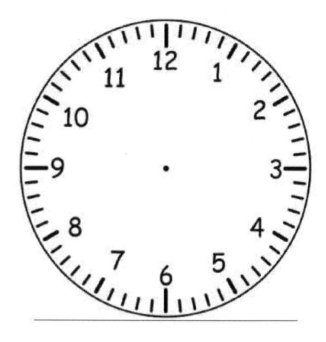

_____

_____

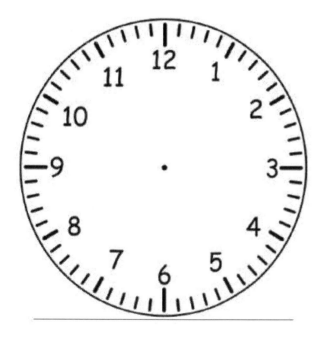

_____

_____

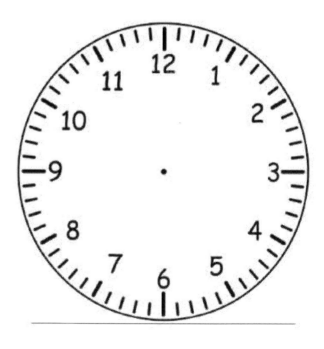

_____

_____

CULTURALLY UPLIFTING FAMILY WORK!

1. Using a paper plate and construction paper, create a model analog clock with identified minutes and hours and the corresponding minute and hour hands to practice telling time. Label the clock hands. Use your kuumba (creativity) to make your clock creative.

2. Laminate a blank medium sized clock that you get off of the internet or another resource. Trim the laminate to the shape of the clock. Using a dry erase maker, create different times and call them out to the watoto (children) for them to write the correct time on a sheet of paper or dry erase board.

3. Read books about Benjamin Banneker to learn more about his life and contributions to society.

4. Hang analog clocks around the house for you and the mtoto (child)/watoto (children) to use to tell time and keep your minds active.

5. Using the internet, books or other resources, conduct research on the ways Black people in Africa historically told time.

6. Using your kuumba, create your own tekhenu (obelisk), sundial, shadow clock and merkhet to tell time.

7. Create your own analog clock puzzle pieces to help watoto learn how to tell time. One side of the puzzle should have the analog clock time and the other side should have the actual time written in numbers.

8. Create a clock without minute and hour hands on the floor and a master list of different times. Ask watoto (children) to make the time with their bodies using the clock on the floor.

9. Create watches with pre-determined times or allow watoto (children) to create their own time and then have them design their own watches and cut them out. Watoto (children) can work together reading each other's watch times and writing them down to see if they can tell the right time. (You can use the sample at the end of book.)

10. Create bingo cards and write different times in the blank bingo spots. Create a master list of times or create mini time sheets that you call out randomly until someone gets bingo. (You can use the sample at the end of book)

ABOUT THE AUTHORS

The Sekou Family is a Black family that lives in Baltimore, Maryland. They believe in the importance of Black families and children connecting, honoring and respecting our cultural heritage and traditions in Africa, America, the Caribbean, and the Diaspora. As a family, we work hard to learn about our cultural heritage and traditions. We practice the Nguzo Saba (The 7 Principles of Blackness) in our everyday lives and give back to our community.

The stories presented in our books are fictionalized accounts based on real events in our family and our journey to live a life that connects, honors, and respects our cultural heritage and traditions. Reading should be a regular occurrence in Black families, and it is important for Black children to see images that look like them in the books they read.

Becoming parents and watching our son, Sekou, grow up inspired these books and the stories in them. Sekou is co-author because he has contributed greatly to the books. Mama and Baba use his name as co-authors of the books to honor his contributions. We use Afrika as our last name to represent our quest to positively uplift our cultural heritage and traditions originating in Africa. Sekou has inspired us to live a life that more closely reflects our beliefs and political ideology. We strongly believe we have to create Black institutions to positively uplift Black families and children, and connect them to their cultural heritage and traditions.

Baba Sekou Afrika, Ed.D. (also known as Julius Davis) is an associate professor of mathematics education at Bowie State University. His scholarship and advocacy focuses on the intellectual and social development of Black boys and young men. He has studied and traveled to Malawi, Tanzania, and Ethiopia on the continent of Africa to learn more about our cultural heritage and traditions.

Mama Sekou Afrika (also known as Yolanda Davis) is a clinical research professional who has studied and traveled to Senegal on the continent of Africa and the Caribbean Islands to learn more about our cultural heritage and traditions.

Sekou Afrika (also known as Sekou Davis) is a student at Ujamaa Shule, the oldest independent Afrikan School in the United States. He plays the Afrikan drums with his brothers and sisters at Ujamaa. To start his formal school-based academic and social development, Sekou attended Watoto Development Center in Baltimore, MD, an Afrikan-centered institution.

Asante Sana (Thank you very much) for practicing Ujamaa (cooperative economics) by purchasing this book and supporting our Black-owned family business. A portion of the proceeds from this book will be used to support and sponsor efforts to culturally uplift Black children and families.

Your Support is Greatly Appreciated!

Baba Sekou Afrika, Mama Sekou Afrika, Sekou Afrika

KUJICHAGULIA PRESS

We define, speak and create for ourselves to celebrate our African and African American cultural heritage and uplift our people using our Kuumba (creativity).

Title: Telling Time with Benjamin Banneker and Sekou
Written by: Baba Sekou Afrika, Mama Sekou Afrika, and Sekou Afrika
Illustrated By: Eloy Claudio
Edited by : Nadirah Angail
Book Design By: Eloy Claudio

Summary: This book will help our children learn the basic concepts of telling time while developing their coloring skills through practice.

ISBN: 978-0-9964595-2-5

For more information or to book an event,
contact Baba/Mama Sekou at books@kujichaguliapress.com.

Kujichagulia Press
P.O. Box 31766
Baltimore, MD 21207
www.kujichaguliapress.com

 KujichaguliaPress   KujichaguliaPress   @Kujichaguliaprs

#TellingTime

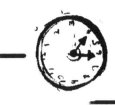
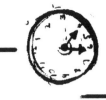
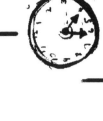

KUJICHAGULIA PRESS
Children's Books

KUJICHAGULIA PRESS

Certificate of Accomplishment

Presented to

Mtoto (Child) Name

For Successfully Completing

TELLING TIME

with BENJAMIN BANNEKER and SEKOU

Activity and Coloring Book

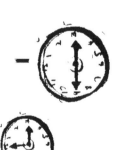
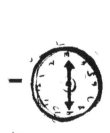
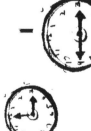

Date

Baba Sekou Afrika

Mama Sekou Afrika

Sekou Afrika

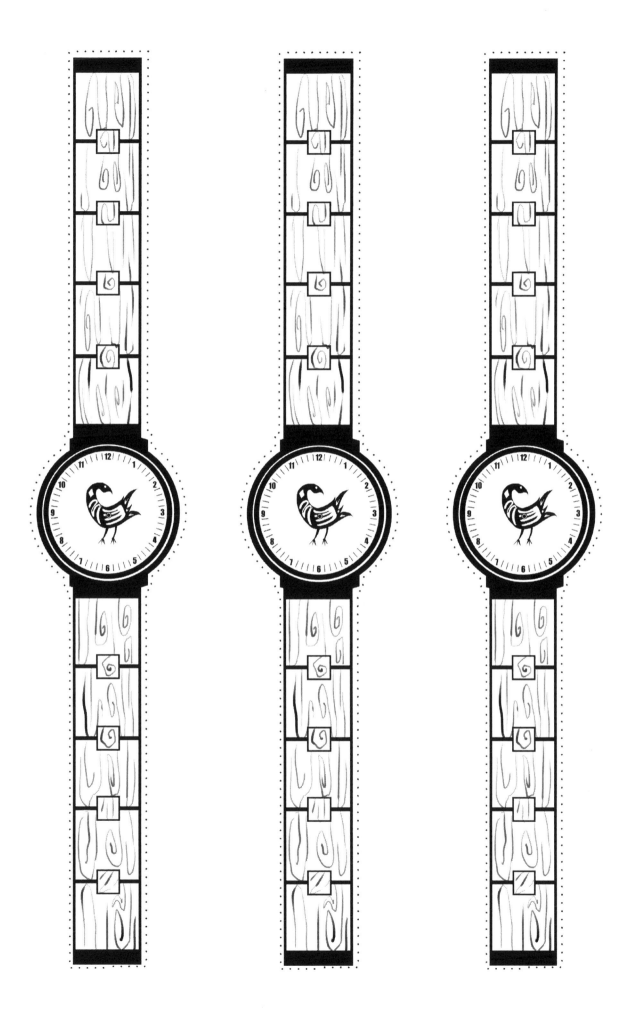

BENJAMIN BANNEKER

TIME BINGO

B	I	N	G	O
		FREE		

Made in the USA
Middletown, DE
11 September 2016